# Physical Electronics

# Physical Electronics

## Brian Tuck and Christos Christopoulos

Department of Electrical and Electronic Engineering,
University of Nottingham

Edward Arnold

© B. Tuck and C. Christopoulos 1986

First published 1986 by
Edward Arnold (Publishers) Ltd
41 Bedford Square, London WC1B 3DQ

Edward Arnold
3 East Read Street, Baltimore, MD 21202, USA

Edward Arnold (Australia) Ltd,
80 Waverley Road, Caulfield East, Victoria 3145, Australia

**British Library Cataloguing in Publication Data**

Tuck, Brian
  Physical electronics.
  1. Electronics
  I. Title  II. Christopoulos, Christos
  537.5       TK7815

ISBN: 0 7131 3587 5

Text set in 10/11pt Times, Linoterm
by Keyset Composition, Colchester, Essex
Printed and bound in Great Britain by the Camelot Press Ltd, Southampton

# Preface

*Physical Electronics* is a text which is suitable for students of Electrical and Electronic Engineering, Physics and other Science and Engineering courses for which a knowledge of Electronics is required. Problems are given at the end of each chapter and tutorial assistance is offered for many of them in the computer package, *Physical Electronics Software.* Answers to all problems are provided at the end of the book. The software package ends with a number of tests which the student can use to assess his grasp of the subject matter.

The teaching of a first course in Electronics is beset with difficulties. The lecturer can present his students with devices such as diodes, transistors, operational amplifiers etc., ready formed, and ask them to believe that the devices can perform certain operations. The course can then proceed to consider how to use them in electronic circuits. Many teachers feel that it is not right to expect a student to accept quite so much on trust and that a more intellectually rigorous approach should be adopted, especially at University level. An alternative method is to give the student a preliminary course in Solid State Physics so that he can grasp how the devices work before starting the study of circuits. The problem here is that the course often takes rather a long time and the student can be left wondering when he will start studying Electronics. In this book, and in the accompanying computer package, we present a compromise which has proved successful at Nottingham for a number of years. The consideration of Solid State Physics is rigorously confined to those aspects which are relevant to the operation of the transistor and its related devices. Within these narrow limits, the approach used is fairly rigorous. This method of presentation allows the lecturer to move in a logical way to the operation of devices and then to the principles of simple amplifying circuits. All this is done in a single course of about 25 lectures.

Thanks are due to Christine Waddon for her quick and accurate preparation of the typescript.
Brian Tuck
Christos Christopoulos
1986

# Contents

# Some useful constants

| | |
|---|---|
| Electron charge, $q$ | $= 1.60 \times 10^{-19}$ C |
| Electron mass, $m_0$ | $= 9.11 \times 10^{-31}$ kg |
| Planck's constant, $h$ | $= 6.63 \times 10^{-34}$ J s |
| Permittivity of free space, $\epsilon_0$ | $= 8.84 \times 10^{-12}$ F m$^{-1}$ |
| Velocity of light in vacuum, $c$ | $= 3.0 \times 10^8$ m s$^{-1}$ |
| Avagadro's number, $N$ | $= 6.02 \times 10^{26}$ (kg mol)$^{-1}$ |
| Boltzmann's constant, $k$ | $= 1.38 \times 10^{-23}$ J K$^{-1}$ |
| 1 electron volt, eV | $1.60 \times 10^{-19}$ J |

## For silicon

| | |
|---|---|
| Band gap | $= 1.1$ eV |
| Electron mobility | $= 0.15$ m$^2$ V$^{-1}$ s$^{-1}$ |
| Hole mobility | $= 0.05$ m$^2$ V$^{-1}$ s$^{-1}$ |
| Electron effective mass | $= 0.4\, m_0$ |
| Intrinsic carrier concentration at 300 K | $= 1.6 \times 10^{16}$ m$^{-3}$ |
| Relative permittivity | $= 11.8$ |
| Density | $= 2400$ kg m$^{-3}$ |

## For germanium

| | |
|---|---|
| Band gap | $= 0.7$ eV |
| Electron mobility | $= 0.39$ m$^2$ V$^{-1}$ s$^{-1}$ |
| Hole mobility | $= 0.19$ m$^2$ V$^{-1}$ s$^{-1}$ |
| Electron effective mass | $= 0.2\, m_0$ |
| Intrinsic carrier concentration at 300 K | $= 2.5 \times 10^{19}$ m$^{-3}$ |
| Relative permittivity | $= 16$ |
| Density | $= 5460$ kg m$^{-3}$ |

# 1 Atoms

## 1.1 Introduction

Semiconductor science and technology constitute one of the wonders of the modern world and nobody who is professionally involved can be other than impressed at the progress that has been made in the last three decades. The results of this technology have entered virtually every home and office and to the uninitiated must appear as nothing less than magic. Most of this progress is due to the increasing sophistication of manufacturing processes based on silicon. In many ways silicon is to this second Industrial Revolution what iron was to the first. It is the most abundant element in the earth's crust after oxygen, relatively easy to extract, and therefore cheap. It is ideally suited to producing the various devices needed in modern electronics: bipolar transistors, field effect transistors, p–n junctions etc. and these devices are now being incorporated on an increasingly fine scale on integrated circuit chips. It must be remembered, however, that some important devices cannot be made from silicon (light-emitting diodes, for instance) and other materials are used in these cases. In addition, a higher performance can sometimes be obtained using other semiconductors; the fastest switching transistors, for instance, are made from gallium arsenide and there is much current interest in this material.

In this book we have the aim of explaining how the most important and basic semiconductor devices work and how they can be used in simple circuits to carry out such operations as amplification. Modest as this aim may seem, we will see that it involves embarking on a fairly long journey. The scenery, however, is fascinating. The start of the journey, inevitably, requires a close look at the properties of the types of materials we are interested in, namely metals and semiconductors. A brief excursion into quantum theory is needed here and this is the subject of the present chapter. We will not study this subject in depth but merely take from it what is needed for further understanding. With an adequate knowledge of atoms we can move on to consider crystals in Chapter 2. The important electronic properties of metals and semiconductors can then be described and the reader should be well on the way to an understanding of the operation and use of transistors.

## 1.2 Quantum theory

Quantum theory provides the basis of the modern theories of matter and of light (or, to be more precise, electromagnetic radiation). It is probably true to say that our view of the physical world is largely determined by the way in which we regard these two topics. Their importance therefore extends far beyond the study of semiconductor devices. We will find that whereas classical physics separated the two phenomena completely, modern physics employs the unifying concept of a wave–particle duality for both.

One hundred years ago there was no need for a 'modern' theory of matter. The old one had sufficed since Newton and it appeared at the time that it always would. It accurately predicted the behaviour of matter from the macroscopic scale of experiments on Earth right up to the motion of the planets. It would not start to show its inadequacies until sub-microscopic phenomena were investigated. Similarly the wave theory of light had been generally accepted since 1801 when Thomas Young in his famous two-slit experiment demonstrated that two beams of light can interfere with each other. Prior to this crucial experiment, the ideas of Newton, whereby light was held to be an aggregate of small corpuscles sent out by the light source, were more generally accepted. It is impossible to explain interference phenomena, however, without resorting to a wave theory of some sort, and in the nineteenth century, the wave theory became firmly established, culminating in Maxwell's prediction of the existence of electromagnetic waves, and Hertz's discovery of them.

Despite the success of the classical theory in explaining the propagation of light, cracks started to appear in the edifice when experiments were carried out to investigate the emission and absorption of radiation by matter. A number of phenomena were observed which completely contradicted the classical theory. Historically the first case of this kind came about with the attempt to account for the radiation emitted by a black body. (A 'black' body is one which absorbs all radiation incident upon it.) Classical physics gave a result which not only disagreed with experiment, but also defied common-sense.

In 1900 Planck presented his treatment of the problem which, by introducing a new idea, provided a formula which agreed completely with experiment. The radiation at frequency $\nu$ is due to an oscillator of that frequency in the radiating source. Planck assumed that the vibrating particles of matter (considered to act as harmonic oscillators) could not emit or absorb radiation continuously, but only in discrete quantities of energy $h\nu$, where $\nu$ is a constant called (subsequently) Planck's constant. The unit of energy $h\nu$ is called a quantum. The hypothesis met initially with much opposition from scientists who saw it as nothing more than a mathematical artifice which happened to give the correct result. However, many phenomena have since been explained using it, and quantum theory has become one of the pillars of modern physics. Two of these phenomena will be described which have particular relevance to the study of semiconductors; the photo-electric effect and the emission and absorption of light by gases. Having established that radiation under certain circumstances possesses particle-like properties, it will then be shown that matter can show properties normally associated with waves.

## 1.3 The photo-electric effect

If an alkali metal is irradiated with ultra-violet light under conditions of vacuum, it is found that electrons are given off from the surface. The emission can be registered as an electric current if a positively-charged electrode is set up close to the surface, as shown in Fig. 1.1. Contrariwise, if the electrode is made sufficiently negative, the current can be arrested. The effect would be expected in broad outline from both the classical and the quantum theories, but it is found that only the latter can fill in the details.

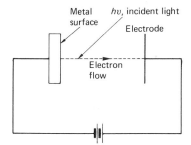

**Fig. 1.1**  Photo-electric effect

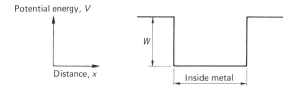

**Fig. 1.2**  Work function for a metal

The effect of the light must be to give energy to electrons inside the metal, allowing them to escape. They require this escape energy because electrons inside the metal are at a lower potential energy than electrons in free space outside the metal. The idea is expressed in Fig. 1.2. This diagram is the first of many which will appear in this book, giving the potential energy for electrons, and it is worth pausing for a moment to make sure that the principle of such diagrams is understood. It goes without saying that there is a force which keeps the electrons inside the metal; if the force did not exist, they would all fall out. The very idea of a force holding in the electrons implies a drop in potential energy, $V$, at the surface, with the force being given by $F = -dV/dx$. The situation of an electron in the metal is analogous to that of a ball resting in a depression in the ground. The ball is at a lower (gravitational) potential than another ball outside the depression, being held there by a force—gravity. It cannot leave the depression unless it is given energy, perhaps by being kicked. In the photo-electric effect the 'kick' is given to the electron by the light.

The important experimental facts about the photo-electric effect are the following:

(i)  In the apparatus of Fig. 1.1, a negative potential can be applied which is just sufficient to stop the flow of current. Let this stopping potential be $V$ volts. If the electrons are emitted from the surface with kinetic energy $E$, then it follows that $E = qV$. The value of $E$ can therefore be found experimentally by measuring $V$. It is found that this energy depends on the frequency of the incident light, $\nu$, according to the formula

$$E = h\nu - W \tag{1.1}$$

where $W$ is a constant of the material, called the work function. The form of the variation is shown in Fig. 1.3. The most important feature of the graph is that below a frequency $\nu_0$, given by $W = h\nu_0$, no electrons are emitted, no matter how intense the light.

(ii) The number of electrons emitted per second, as revealed by the current flow, is proportional to the intensity of the incident light.

The phenomenon was explained very simply by Einstein, using the quantum hypothesis of Planck. He took the idea one step further, however, postulating quantum properties not just for the processes of emission and absorption of radiation, but as an inherent quality of light. He put forward a theory of light quanta (photons) in which he suggested that light consists of

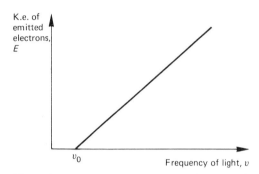

**Fig. 1.3**

corpuscles, of energy $h\nu$, which fly through space like a hail of shot, with the velocity of light. A hypothesis very like that of Newton, in fact. Photons have other interesting properties. Since they travel with the speed of light then, according to the theory of relativity, they must be particles of zero mass. They do, however, have momentum $p$, given by $p = h/\lambda$, where $\lambda$ is the wavelength of the light.

Once the hypothesis is accepted, the photo-electric effect becomes clear. Photons, each of energy $h\nu$, fall upon the sample. The more intense the light, the more photons impinge on the surface per second. A photon can interact with an electron, giving up its energy. The electrons in the metal are down an energy well, depth $W$. Providing $h\nu > W$, an electron can be given enough energy to leave the metal, and the 'spare' energy will appear as kinetic energy. If the light is made more intense, then more electrons are ejected. However, if $h\nu < W$, a photon cannot liberate an electron, no matter how intense the light. (The probability of two photons combining to liberate an electron is small enough to be ignored.)

Simple and elegant as this explanation is, it is necessary to examine the wave theory to see if it can provide any explanation for the photo-electric effect. According to the wave theory, a light wave carries energy which is proportional to the intensity of the wave. When light is absorbed in a metal, some of this can be given to an electron, which eventually acquires enough energy to leave the metal. It is very difficult to explain why this process should have anything to do with the wavelength of light; one would expect only the energy of the beam (i.e. the intensity of the light) to matter. The most striking contradiction between the two theories, however, concerns the timing of the electron emission. According to the wave theory, an electron in the metal absorbs energy from the incident wave until enough has been accumulated for emission to occur. This process takes a certain amount of time, which can be calculated for a given experimental situation. The photon theory describes electron emission as a single-stage process, occurring because of the collision of two particles; a photon and an electron. The process should therefore be virtually instantaneous upon turning on the light.

This contradiction between the two theories suggests an experiment which was, in fact, carried out in 1914 by Meyer and Gerlach. They observed the photo-electric effect using fine metallic dust particles as specimens. Knowing the intensity of the light and the dimensions of the particles, they could calculate the minimum irradiation time required for a particle to absorb sufficient energy to emit an electron. According to wave theory this amounted to several seconds; according to photon theory, as noted above, it should happen almost instantaneously. Their technique for establishing the time of electron ejection was interesting. They suspended charged metal dust particles in a vertical electric field, the electric field just counteracting the force of gravity. A fresh emission of an electron from one of these particles was shown by an acceleration of the particle in the field, due to the increased positive charge of the particle.

The result of the experiment was quite unambiguous; in every case they observed electron emission as soon as irradiation started. Thus the phenomenon which is explained so simply using Einstein's photon theory cannot be explained using classical wave theory. However, before abandoning too promptly all thoughts of wave motion, let us recall that interference phenomena still exist, phenomena which are quite inexplicable unless one attributes some wave-like property to light. It seems necessary, therefore, to credit light with some particle-like and some wave-like properties.

## 1.4  Emission and absorption spectra of gases

If an electric current is passed through a gas or vapour, light is usually given out, the colour of which is characteristic of the composition of the gas. The yellow colour of the sodium vapour lamp is a good example. The phenomenon is widely used nowadays for lighting purposes, especially office and street lighting. If light from a gas discharge tube is passed through a spectrometer, the spectrum consists not of a continuous output, but of a number of discrete wavelengths, a given set of wavelengths being peculiar to a given element in the gas. This is usually called a 'line' spectrum.

The experiment can be turned round by shining light with a continuous spectrum through the gas and analysing what comes out the other side. This time, the spectrometer reveals a continuous spectrum with certain wavelengths missing. This is called an absorption spectrum. In short, it is found that a gas can emit light only at certain wavelengths and can also absorb light only of those same wavelengths. The absorption and emission spectra must be caused by atoms taking in or giving out energy. Since the wavelengths are characteristic of the element concerned, this information must tell us something about the internal structure of the atom. Once again we will find that classical ideas are not adequate to explain the phenomenon. The discussion will be confined to hydrogen, the simplest atom.

The first 'modern' picture of an atom was put forward by Rutherford in 1911. Such an atom has a central nucleus of small dimensions ($10^{-13}$–$10^{-12}$ cm) around which move a number of electrons, $Z$ say. The electron orbits are of atomic dimensions, i.e. of the order of $10^{-8}$ cm. The nucleus carries a charge $Zq$ to counteract the combined charge of the electrons, $-Zq$. Almost all of the mass of the atom resides in the nucleus. For the case of hydrogen, $Z = 1$. The analogy with the solar system is obvious (and understandable), but the model soon runs into trouble. The stability of atoms, for instance, is not explained. The hydrogen atom consists of a single electron rotating about its nucleus. By the rules of electromagnetism, such a rotating charge should continuously give out radiation. Let us consider the consequences of this statement. The frequency of the radiation must be equal to the orbital frequency of the electron. (The simplest way to see this is to look at the atom edgeways-on. The electron is then seen to be moving with simple harmonic motion about the centre and acting just like a transmitting aerial.) Since the electron is continuously giving out energy, it becomes steadily less energetic itself, so the radius continually decreases. Hence a continuously variable frequency should be obtained. This prediction is contrary to experiment and, worse still, the electron presumably spirals into the nucleus and destroys itself. We are thus led to the conclusion that matter is unstable, an assertion that we are bound to reject.

## 1.5  Bohr theory of the hydrogen atom

The theory was a first attempt to remove the above anomalies. It is important historically because it represents an intermediate stage between classical theory and modern quantum theory. It also has the great virtue of being easy to understand. The Rutherford model of a hydrogen atom is used with an electron making a circular orbit around the nucleus. There are three postulates:

(i) The radius of an orbit is restricted to certain fixed values and no emission or absorption takes place while the electron remains in one of them. This removes, in the grand manner, the difficulty about the electron spiralling in to the nucleus. The theory simply postulates that it does not happen.

(ii) When the electron changes from one stable orbit to another, emission or absorption of a photon takes place. The frequency of the light, $\nu$, is given by

$$h\nu = \frac{hc}{\lambda} = E_a - E_b \qquad (1.2)$$

where $E_a$, $E_b$ are the energies of the electron in orbits $a$ and $b$ respectively, and $h$ is Planck's constant.

(iii) The angular momentum of an allowed orbit must be an integral number $\times h/2\pi$.

i.e.    $mvr = \dfrac{nh}{2\pi}$    $n = 1, 2, 3, \ldots$        (1.3)

where $m$ is the mass of the electron, $v$ is its velocity and $r$ is the radius of its orbit. It is this postulate that puts a restriction on the allowed orbits and tells us what the allowed radii are.

Consider a hydrogen atom with the electron in one of its allowed orbits. For equilibrium, the acceleration of the electron towards the centre must be given by the Coulombic attraction, i.e.

$$\frac{mv^2}{r} = \frac{q^2}{4\pi\epsilon_0 r^2} \qquad\qquad (1.4)$$

where $\epsilon_0$ is the permittivity of free space. Eliminating $v$ between equations (1.3) and (1.4) gives

$$r_n = \frac{n^2 h^2 \epsilon_0}{\pi m q^2} \qquad\qquad (1.5)$$

where the subscript '$n$' is introduced to indicate that there are an infinite number of possible values of $r$, corresponding to all possible integer values of $n$. Equation (1.5) shows that the smallest orbit corresponds to putting $n = 1$. All other constants are known, so $r_1$ can be calculated. It comes out to 0.053 nm, and this length is usually called a Bohr radius. In addition

$r_2 = 4r_1$

$r_3 = 9r_1$ etc.

### 1.5.1 Energy

The total energy of the electron is the sum of its kinetic and potential energies.

Kinetic energy $= \dfrac{1}{2}mv^2 = \dfrac{q^2}{8\pi\epsilon_0 r_n}$

where the second equality is obtained by substituting for $mv^2$ using equation (1.4). The potential energy of the electron is the potential of a charge $-q$ in the Coulombic field of the nucleus of charge $+q$. This is $-q^2/4\pi\epsilon_0 r_n$. Hence the total energy, $E_n$ is given by:

$$E_n = \frac{-q^2}{8\pi\epsilon_0 r_n} \qquad\qquad (1.6)$$

Substituting from equation (1.5) for $r_n$ gives the alternative form:

$$E_n = \frac{-mq^4}{8n^2 h^2 \epsilon_0^2} \qquad\qquad (1.7)$$

It is important to realise why this number must be negative. We take as our zero of energy the energy of an electron at rest an infinite distance from the nucleus. In this context, an 'infinite' distance can be interpreted as one at which the electron is substantially unaffected by the field of the nucleus. An electron at rest 'outside' the atom therefore has zero energy. An electron 'inside' the atom must have less energy than this, for the same reason that electrons inside a metal must have less energy than electrons outside; if it were not so, the electron would not stay within the atom. A diagram of the general type of Fig. 1.2 must therefore apply, with static electrons outside the atom having zero energy and those inside having negative energy. The lowest allowed energy is therefore the one with the largest negative value, i.e. $E_1$.

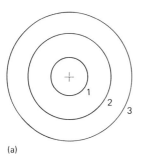

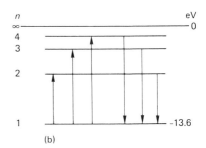

(a)                                    (b)

**Fig. 1.4**  Bohr model of hydrogen atom

The Bohr picture is thus one of a series of circular orbits, radius $r_1$, $r_2$, $r_3$ etc., of energy $E_1$, $E_2$, $E_3$ etc. A given atom can, of course, only be in one of these allowed 'states' at any one time (see Fig. 1.4(a)). The innermost orbit, given by $n = 1$, is called the ground state for the atom and, since it is the lowest energy state, it is the one in which an atom normally exists unless it is disturbed from the outside. Putting $n = 1$ in equation (1.7) gives $E_1 = -2.18 \times 10^{-18}$ J or, to use a more convenient unit for energy, $E_1 = -13.6$ eV. (An electron-volt is the energy acquired by an electron falling through a potential of one volt; $1$ eV $= 1.6 \times 10^{-19}$ J.)

The energies are most conveniently expressed in the energy-level diagram of Fig. 1.4(b). The levels get closer together as $n$ gets larger, converging to $E = 0$ as $n \rightarrow \infty$. Positive values of energy correspond to electrons which are 'free', i.e. which do not belong to any atom. Such an electron can have any kinetic energy, so above $E = 0$ there is a continuum of states. Giving an electron in the ground state an energy of 13.6 eV or more removes it completely from the hydrogen atom, which becomes an ion. 13.6 eV is therefore called the ionisation energy for hydrogen.

### 1.5.2  Emission and absorption

We are now in a position to consider the emission and absorption of radiation. According to Bohr's second postulate, the atom can only absorb energy by the electron being excited from a lower to a higher energy level. Similarly it can only emit energy by relaxing from a higher to a lower one. It is clear that such a model gives rise to line rather than continuous spectra. In order for the gas to fluoresce, therefore, it is necessary to excite some of the atoms. This can be accomplished, for instance, by passing a current through the gas. Collisions take place between atoms and the current-carrying electrons, causing excitation, as shown by the upward arrows on Fig. 1.4(b). When the atoms relax, the emitted photon frequencies are those corresponding to downward arrows on the diagram, e.g.

$$h\nu_{21} = E_2 - E_1$$
$$h\nu_{31} = E_3 - E_1$$
$$h\nu_{41} = E_4 - E_1 \text{ etc.}$$

Similarly there is another series of emitted frequencies terminating on the second level; $\nu_{32}$, $\nu_{42}$, $\nu_{52}$ etc. Using equation (1.7) for the energy levels, we can write a general expression for the discrete photon frequencies emitted by the hydrogen atom:

$$E_a - E_b = h\nu_{ab} = \frac{mq^4}{8\epsilon_0^2 h^2}\left(\frac{1}{b^2} - \frac{1}{a^2}\right)$$

It is interesting to note that an equation of this form was deduced empirically from the experimental work on the hydrogen atom some years before the advent of Bohr theory.

### 1.5.3  Other atoms

The Bohr theory is worked out for a single electron rotating around a positive nucleus. To carry out a calculation for an atom of greater atomic number is much more difficult. In helium, for example, an electron is not only in the Coulombic field of the positive nucleus, but also in the field of the other electron. Hydrogen is therefore the only neutral atom the theory applies to. However, the ions $He^+$ and $Li^{++}$, for instance, both have a single electron and the theory can easily be adapted for the greater number of positive charges in the nucleus. Suppose there are $Z$ positive charges around which a single electron orbits; equation (1.4) becomes

$$\frac{mv^2}{r} = \frac{Zq^2}{4\pi\epsilon_0 r^2}$$

and working through in the same way leads to the equation

$$h\nu_{ab} = \frac{Z^2 mq^4}{8\epsilon_0^2 h^2}\left(\frac{1}{b^2} - \frac{1}{a^2}\right) \tag{1.9}$$

### 1.5.4  Comparison with experiment

The Bohr theory represents a great step forward in our understanding of the atom. It predicts the existence of line spectra and describes the emissions from

H, He$^+$ and Li$^{++}$ very well. The calculated ionisation energy of hydrogen, 13.6 eV, agrees well with experiment. There are difficulties of principle in accepting the theory, however. The first postulate amounts to a direct and unexplained contradiction to the classical theory. The quantisation rule for angular momentum, also, is produced with the air of a conjuror pulling a rabbit out of a hat. Perhaps more serious than these rather aesthetic worries is the fact that closer examination of the experimental evidence reveals features that are not predicted by the theory. The emission lines are found to have a fine structure, i.e. many of them really consist of a number of lines, very close together in wavelength. This must reflect back to the energy level scheme of Fig. 1.4(b) and suggests that the energy levels themselves have a fine structure. Further fine structure is obtained in the emission spectrum if a magnetic field is applied.

Efforts were made to improve Bohr theory to account for these phenomena, but the efforts became largely irrelevant with the general acceptance of the wave-mechanical approach to atoms. This is not to say, however, that Bohr theory is just a scientific dinosaur. It still has its uses as a good simple approximation in many situations. It will be used in this way in Chapter 4.

## 1.6 Matter waves

The way in which light appears to behave sometimes as waves and sometimes as corpuscles is one of the most remarkable results of quantum theory. Having accepted this idea, nothing is sacred, and it becomes worthwhile to consider whether matter also plays this dual role. The idea is attractive because it suggests the possibility of establishing a unified theory of wave-corpuscles which applies both to matter and to radiation. This line of thought was pursued by De Broglie, who put forward his ideas about matter waves in 1924. He postulated that there is a wave associated with a particle of matter just as there is one associated with a photon. To make the theoretical bridge between the wave and particle pictures he suggested that the same equation relating momentum, $p$, to wavelength, $\lambda$, applies in both cases, i.e.

$$p = \frac{h}{\lambda} \tag{1.10}$$

A major difference between matter waves and light waves must be noted, however. Photons always travel with the speed of light, whereas matter can travel at any speed. The particle speed in the corpuscle picture for matter corresponds to the group velocity of the wave in the wave picture.

Let us calculate the wavelength associated with a beam of particles. It is convenient to choose electrons for the calculation because a beam of reasonably uniform energy can be produced by accelerating them through a potential $V$. Suppose that at the end of the acceleration they have velocity $v$, then

$$\frac{1}{2}mv^2 = qV \tag{1.11}$$

from equation (1.10),

$$\lambda = \frac{h}{mv} \tag{1.12}$$

Substituting in (1.12) for $v$, using (1.11)

$$\lambda = \frac{h}{(2mqV)^{\frac{1}{2}}} \tag{1.13}$$

Putting in the values for $m, q, h$, the equation becomes

$$\lambda = \frac{1.226}{V^{\frac{1}{2}}} \, \text{nm} \tag{1.14}$$

where $V$ is in volts. Thus if a beam of electrons is accelerated through 100 volts, the associated matter wave, as predicted by the De Broglie relations, has wavelength 0.123 nm. The wavelength corresponds roughly to X-ray wavelengths, although it is important to realise that matter waves are not X-rays.

### 1.6.1  Diffraction of matter waves

It has been remarked above that the acid test for a wave model is to see whether or not interference phenomena occur. Davisson and Germer (1927) accelerated electrons through potentials of the order of 100–200 V and made

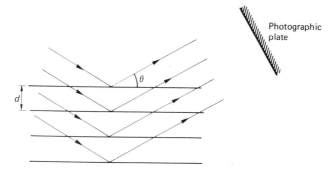

**Fig. 1.5**  Diffraction of X-rays

them impinge on the surface of a nickel specimen. The directions in which electrons were back-scattered from the crystal were detected using a screen. Before outlining their results, it is necessary to say something about the diffraction of X-rays by crystals, which turns out to give very similar results.

Consider the experiment shown in Fig. 1.5. X-rays, wavelength $\lambda$, are shone onto a crystal, making an angle $\theta$ with the set of planes shown. A photographic plate is placed to detect any X-rays 'reflected' from the set of planes. If there is a reflected ray it gives a spot on the plate. It is found that there is a reflected ray only if the following condition is satisfied

$$n\lambda = 2d \sin \theta \qquad n = 1, 2, 3 \ldots \tag{1.15}$$

where $d$ is the spacing of the planes doing the reflecting. Equation (1.15) is called Bragg's law. There are many sets of low index planes in a crystal; Fig. 1.5 shows only one such set. Any set which obeys Bragg's law will give rise to a spot on the photographic plate and the pattern of spots which is obtained is called a diffraction pattern.

Davisson and Germer found that their detector showed just the same pattern of spots that would have been given if X-rays had been used instead of an electron beam. They concluded that diffraction had occurred and, furthermore, were able to use equation (1.15) to calculate the wavelength of the electron wave. Upon doing this, they found exactly the same value as that given by equation (1.14) which was derived using De Broglie's hypothesis.

It remained to establish that the observed phenomenon was a property of all matter and not simply of electrons. To this end, diffraction experiments have been carried out using beams of neutrons and even using molecular rays of hydrogen and helium. In all cases the results confirmed the De Broglie hypothesis, i.e. interference effects were observed. The fact that positive results were obtained using molecules is especially significant. Here, surely, the experiment was carried out using matter in the normal sense of the word. If a molecular ray of helium atoms is intercepted after being diffracted at a crystal surface and collected in a jar, we find a gas with the normal chemical properties. These diffraction experiments constituted a triumphant confirmation of De Broglie's ideas, and it is important to realise that his hypothesis refers not just to very small particles, but to all matter. The wave-like behaviour only becomes observable, however, when the mass of the particle concerned is very small.

The technique of electron diffraction has proved to be so useful that it is now used in many laboratories in a routine manner. The use of electron rather than X-ray diffraction in studying the structure of solids has much to recommend it. Very high intensities can be achieved in electron beams, so exposure times for photographing diffraction patterns are much shorter. In addition, the wavelength can be adjusted simply by varying the voltage on the apparatus. There is no known method for constructing lenses for X-rays; electron beams, on the other hand, can easily be focussed using electric and magnetic fields. Microscopes can therefore be made using electron matter waves instead of light waves. Modern electron microscopes use accelerating voltages in the region of 100 kV, i.e. wavelengths of about 0.004 nm. Because of the small wavelength, these microscopes have much higher resolving powers than optical microscopes.

## 1.7 Hydrogen atom using the concept of matter waves

The idea of describing matter by matter waves leads to a completely new way of looking at the subject and gives rise to a branch of mathematical physics called either wave mechanics or quantum mechanics, depending on the formalism used. This is an interesting, if difficult, study which we cannot pursue here because it would take us too far from our intended path. It is worth trying to apply the matter wave idea directly to the Bohr model, however. This is a highly disreputable procedure, since it amounts to mixing

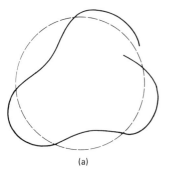
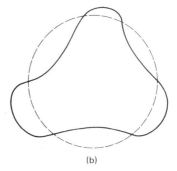

(a)                                              (b)

**Fig. 1.6** Matter wave concept applied to Bohr atom

up two different theories. It is justified here on the grounds that it gives a simple insight into wave mechanics and that this book is written by engineers. Consider a hydrogen atom with the electron in one of its allowed Bohr orbits (or 'stationary states'). According to De Broglie the electron can also be described as a matter wave circling the centre. Figure 1.6(a) shows what happens if the length of the orbit does not correspond to an integral number of matter wavelengths; interference takes place, destroying the matter wave, and a stationary state cannot exist. Figure 1.6(b) shows the stable condition which is obtained when the orbit just contains an integral number of wavelengths. The condition for a stable state is therefore

$$2\pi r = n\lambda \qquad n = 1, 2, 3 \ldots \tag{1.16}$$

Substituting the De Broglie equation, (1.10), gives

$$\text{angular momentum} = mvr = \frac{nh}{2\pi} \tag{1.3}$$

which is the Bohr condition, not pulled out of a hat, but presented with at least some semblance of logic, based on the idea of the matter wave.

### 1.7.1  Wave-mechanical solution for the hydrogen atom

It has been noted above that wave mechanics can be a difficult subject. In fact it is often easy to use the theory to write down a mathematical description of the physical problem. The difficulty arises when one tries to find solutions to the equations which are obtained. Fortunately the hydrogen atom provides an example of a physical situation that can be solved completely and analytically. We will not give the solution here; it can be found in most textbooks on wave mechanics. Instead we will simply give the important results.

The most striking aspect of the wave-mechanical solution is its vagueness. According to the Bohr theory, an electron in one of its allowed states orbits with a precisely defined radius. The wave theory, on the other hand, deals in probabilities. It permits the electron to be at any point in space and gives a value for the probability of its being there. The solution for the ground state of the hydrogen atom is particularly simple, since it is spherically symmetrical, i.e. the probability depends only on the distance of the electron from the nucleus. It happens that for this state the 'most probable' distance of the electron from the nucleus is one Bohr radius. This is shown in Fig. 1.7. This idea of the electron being allowed to be anywhere in space is not as outrageous as it first seems, since the function shown drops off very sharply with distance, so that the probability of the electron being found several Bohr radii from the nucleus is very small (although not zero).

The wave-mechanical solution gives rise to quantum numbers in the same way that Bohr theory does, but whereas the latter gives just one, namely '$n$', the former gives three. This should not be thought of as arbitrary in any sense; the wave-mechanical description of the hydrogen atom is three-dimensional and it is found that each dimension gives rise to a quantum number. In

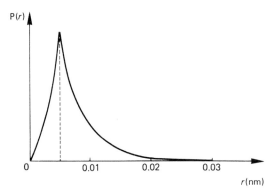

**Fig. 1.7** Probability of an electron in the ground state of an H atom being distance $r$ from nucleus. Dotted line indicates one Bohr radius

addition, a fourth quantum number arises because of the separate phenomenon of electron 'spin'. The four numbers can be described as follows.

(i) *Principal quantum number, n*
This is essentially Bohr's quantum number. It plays the major role in determining the energy of a stable state. As in Bohr theory, it must be an integer.

(ii) *Angular momentum quantum number, l*
In Bohr theory, a single value of orbital angular momentum relates to a single value of energy. Once the restriction is removed that the electron must rotate in a circle, it is found that a given value of $n$ can have several different values of orbital momentum. It works out that the angular momentum of a state is given by $\sqrt{l(l+1)} \times (h/2\pi)$, where $l$ is also an integer and is permitted to have the values $0, 1, 2, \ldots (n-1)$.

Two points are worth noting here. The first is that the quantity $h/2\pi$ is found once again as the 'natural' unit of angular momentum. The second is that zero angular momentum is permitted, a rather unusual idea which again underlines the fact that the electron is not orbiting the nucleus in this model.

It is found that the value of $l$ has a small effect on the energy so that, for instance, the state described by $n = 2, l = 0$ has a slightly different energy to that described by $n = 2, l = 1$. This is shown in Fig. 1.8, in which the differences are somewhat exaggerated to make the point clear. Note that, for reasons which are almost lost in the mists of time, an electron in an $l = 0$ state is described as an s electron and that the letters p, d, f, are similarly associated with $l$ values of 1, 2, 3. It is clear from Fig. 1.8 that a fine structure has now been introduced into the energy-level scheme so that, for instance, the emission spectrum due to electrons relaxing from $n = 3$ to $n = 2$ could have up to six lines, slightly separated from each other in wavelength. (In fact, for rather complicated reasons, less than six would be observed in practice.) It will be remembered that the downfall of the Bohr theory was due to the experimental observation of just such a fine structure in emission spectra.

(iii) *Magnetic quantum number, m*

If a magnetic field is applied to a gas then it is found that yet more fine structure appears in the emission spectrum. It is clear from the above that this implies further structure in the energy levels. The phenomenon can be explained as follows. The angular momentum discussed in the previous

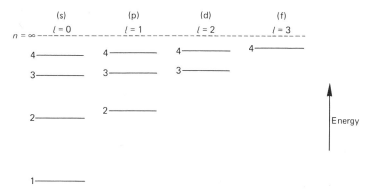

**Fig. 1.8**

section is a property of a charged particle, namely an electron. This implies that a magnetic moment must also exist. Angular momentum is a vector quantity, so it has a direction in space. Similarly the magnetic moment of the atom is a vector in the same direction as the angular momentum, and proportional to it in magnitude. This can best be seen by returning to the Bohr picture of an electron circling the nucleus. The angular momentum vector is, by definition, perpendicular to the plane of rotation. The motion of the electron creates a circular current, rather as if the atom were a minute ring of superconducting wire. Elementary physics tells us that in this situation the atom must become a small magnet, with a north pole on one side of the plane of rotation and a south pole on the other. The direction of the magnetic moment is therefore the same as that of the $l$-vector. Since both the current and the angular momentum are proportional to the speed of the electron, it follows that magnetic moment and angular momentum are proportional to each other.

In the absence of fields there is no preferred direction for the $l$-vector so in a large collection of atoms the vectors are randomly distributed. If an external magnetic field is applied, then common sense tells us that all of the small magnets should line up with the field, i.e. all of the *l*-vectors should be in the same direction. Unfortunately common sense lets us down with distressing regularity when sub-microscopic phenomena are studied, and this case is no exception. According to quantum theory, none of the *l*-vectors line up with the field, but they do adopt certain specific directions with respect to it. These directions are defined by the component of the *l*-vector in the direction of the field which is permitted the values $mh/2\pi$, where $m = -l, -(l-1)\ldots0\ldots(l-1), l$.

The rule is best understood by taking an example. Consider an electron in a state described by $l = 2$. The length of the *l*-vector is $\sqrt{l(l+1)} \times (h/2\pi)$, i.e. $2.45 \times (h/2\pi)$. According to the rule, the vector can only take up directions for which the component along the field is one of the following:

$$(-2, -1, 0, +1, +2) \times \frac{h}{2\pi}$$

The physical picture is given in Fig. 1.9. The five numbers inside the bracket are called magnetic quantum numbers, *m*.

Although there are five possibilities in this case, it would be wrong to assume that 20% of the *l*-vectors line up in each permitted direction. The energy of state E, for instance, is very much greater than that of state A; it is almost lining up counter to the field (Fig. 1.9). Most of the atoms will be in state A, therefore, with progressively fewer in B, C, D, E.

(iv) *Electron spin angular momentum, s*

More refined experiments show that the above three quantum numbers do not completely account for the fine structure in emission spectra. The phenomena are completely explained, however, if it is assumed that the electron itself has angular momentum, quite separate from the momentum of rotation. Because it is convenient to put a physical interpretation on the rather abstract ideas, it is usual to talk of the electron having a 'spin' about its axis. The

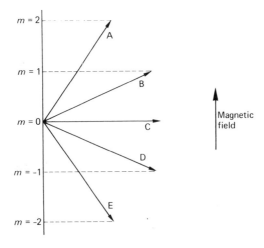

**Fig. 1.9**

electron can spin either clockwise or anti-clockwise with values $\pm(\frac{1}{2} \times (h/2\pi))$. This gives rise to the spin quantum number, $s$, which can be $+\frac{1}{2}$ or $-\frac{1}{2}$.

### 1.7.2  Summary of quantum rules

An electron in a hydrogen atom is characterised by a set of four numbers, $n, l, m, s$, which are permitted to have the following values:

$$n = 1, 2, 3, 4 \ldots$$
$$l = 0, 1, 2, \ldots (n-1)$$
$$m = -l, -(l-1), \ldots 0 \ldots (l-1), l$$
$$s = +\tfrac{1}{2} \text{ or } -\tfrac{1}{2}$$

## 1.8  Many-electron atoms

Much of the above theory, worked out for the hydrogen atom, can be shown to carry over to many-electron atoms. Each electron in a given atom is 'labelled' with a set of four quantum numbers. Conventionally, electrons with the same value of $n$ are said to be in the same 'shell' and those with the same values of $n$ and $l$ are in the same 'sub-shell'.

### 1.8.1  The Pauli exclusion principle

This deceptively simple rule is one of the most important in science. It states that no two electrons in the same atom can have the same set of four quantum numbers. Once this principle is accepted the Periodic Table follows as a logical consequence. The first thing to note is that according to the rules of Section 1.7.2, each sub-shell has a maximum permitted number of electrons. A $p$ shell (i.e. $l = 1$), for instance, has the possibilities $m = -1, 0, +1$, with each having a spin of $+\frac{1}{2}$ or $-\frac{1}{2}$, giving a maximum of six electrons in all. The maximum numbers in the first three shells are therefore as follows

| $n = 1$ | $n = 2$ | | $n = 3$ | | | |
|---------|---------|--------|---------|--------|---------|-----|
| $l = 0$ | $l = 0$ | $l = 1$ | $l = 0$ | $l = 1$ | $l = 2$ | etc. |
| 2 | 2 | 6 | 2 | 6 | 10 | |

In general, electrons with lower $n$ have lower energies and, within a given shell, electrons with lower $l$ have lower energies. (This simple rule starts to break down a little for atomic numbers above 18, but this need not concern us here.) Thus hydrogen, with its single electron, is defined by $n = 1, l = 0$ in its ground state or, to use the traditional nomenclature, it is in a 1s state. Helium has a second electron which can also occupy a 1s state, so the atom can be described as $1s^2$. Lithium, with an atomic number of three, must have its third electron in the next sub-shell and is therefore described as $1s^2 2s^1$. And so on, filling up from the left. In this way, the whole Periodic Table emerges. Table 1.1 shows the first few elements and one or two of interest of higher atomic

**Table 1.1**

| Atomic number | Element | 1st shell $n = 1$ $l = 0$ | 2nd shell $n = 2$ $l = 0$ $l = 1$ | | 3rd shell $n = 3$ $l = 0$ $l = 1$ $l = 2$ | | | 4th shell $n = 4$ $l = 0$ $l = 1$ $l = 2$ $l = 3$ | | | |
|---|---|---|---|---|---|---|---|---|---|---|---|
| 1 | H | 1 | | | | | | | | | |
| 2 | He | 2 | | | | | | | | | |
| 3 | Li | 2 | 1 | | | | | | | | |
| 4 | Be | 2 | 2 | | | | | | | | |
| 5 | B | 2 | 2 | 1 | | | | | | | |
| 6 | C | 2 | 2 | 2 | | | | | | | |
| 10 | Ne | 2 | 2 | 6 | | | | | | | |
| 11 | Na | 2 | 2 | 6 | 1 | | | | | | |
| 14 | Si | 2 | 2 | 6 | 2 | 2 | | | | | |
| 32 | Ge | 2 | 2 | 6 | 2 | 6 | 10 | 2 | 2 | | |

number. Some of the basic properties of matter appear immediately from the Table, e.g.

1  Since a completely full shell is a very stable structure, elements with this property would be expected to be reluctant to exchange electrons with other elements, i.e. involve themselves in chemical reactions. A glance at the Table shows that the elements with full shells are indeed the so-called 'inert' gases such as helium and neon.

2  By the same argument it would be expected that an element with a single electron outside a completely full shell would be highly reactive from the chemical point of view. The atoms in this category are the alkali metals and two (lithium and sodium) are shown in the Table. These elements have a high probability of taking part in chemical reactions in which they lose the outermost electron.

3  Some elements have four electrons in the outer shell. Examples in Table 1.1 are carbon, silicon and germanium. This leads to a tetragonal crystal structure usually called the diamond structure, which will be discussed in the next chapter. These elements also have similar electronic properties; silicon and germanium are both semiconductors and the diamond form of carbon has many semiconductor-like features.

We now leave the study of individual atoms and consider what happens when they join together to form crystalline solids.

## 1.9  Problems

Problems marked * are considered in the computer package (see Preface).

**1.1*** When a metal surface is illuminated with light of frequency 900 THz $(900 \times 10^{12}$ Hz), electrons are emitted which may be stopped by a potential 0.60 V. When the same surface is illuminated with light of frequency 1260 THz, the required stopping potential is 2.1 V. Calculate the value of Planck's constant and the work function of the metal in volts.

**1.2** Assuming that the motion of electron waves is circular, calculate the following parameters for the ground state of the hydrogen atom:
    (a) principal quantum number,    (g) force on the electron,

(b) orbital radius,
(c) angular momentum,
(d) linear momentum,
(e) angular velocity,
(f) linear speed,

(h) acceleration of the electron,
(i) kinetic energy,
(j) potential energy,
(k) total energy.

**1.3** A photon, incident upon a hydrogen atom, ejects an electron with an emitted kinetic energy of 10.7 eV. If the electron had been in the first excited state, calculate
  (i) the energy of the photon,
  (ii) the energy with which an electron from the ground state would be emitted when excited by a similar photon.

**1.4** (a) Compute the de Broglie wavelength of protons moving at $1.32 \times 10^5 \, \text{m s}^{-1}$.
    (b) If the protons had been accelerated from rest by a potential difference, what was the potential difference required to reach the above velocity?

**1.5** The resolving power of a microscope is the smallest distance that can be resolved or distinguished. It is approximately equal to the wavelength of the light used. In an electron microscope, a beam of electrons substitutes for the light photons, and the glass lenses are replaced by electrical and magnetic focusing fields. A narrow beam of electrons with kinetic energies of about 100 000 eV is incident on the thin specimen to be examined.
  Calculate the theoretical lower limit of the resolving power due to the wave properties of the electrons. By what factor is this better than the present experimental optimum of about 0.6 nm?

**1.6** State clearly the three basic postulates of the Bohr theory and indicate the type of atom to which the theory applies.
  Starting from the postulates, derive an expression for the allowed values of the orbital radius of an electron, and hence calculate the minimum radius of rotation of an electron in the $\text{He}^+$ ion, according to Bohr theory.

# 2 Crystals

Most metals and semiconductors occur naturally as solids with fairly simple crystal structures. In general, it can be stated that the structures which are found represent the lowest energy configurations which the atoms can assume. In this chapter we first consider the forces which hold together the various types of crystal then look at the most common crystal structures and the formalism which is used to describe them. Finally, we briefly consider imperfections which occur in real crystals.

## 2.1 Bonding

Four main types of bonding occur: ionic, covalent, metallic and Van der Waals. The first three are important in metals and semiconductors. 'Hybrid' bonding also occurs, so that the semiconductor GaAs, for instance, has part covalent and part ionic bonding.

### 2.1.1 Ionic bonding

This is found in compounds such as NaCl and KCl, which are often described as being of the I-VII type, since sodium and potassium come from group I of the Periodic Table and chlorine is in group VII. It is also found in II-VI compounds such as MgO. Let us take KCl as an example. Using the nomenclature outlined in Chapter 1, the individual atoms can be described thus:

$$K \quad 1s^2 \quad 2s^2 \quad 2p^6 \quad 3s^2 \quad 3p^6 \quad 4s^1$$
$$Cl \quad 1s^2 \quad 2s^2 \quad 2p^6 \quad 3s^2 \quad 3p^5$$

(Note that with the K atom we have one of the complications hinted at in the previous chapter; the 19th electron goes into the 4s sub-shell instead of the expected 3d.) Each of the atoms is within one electron of having a completely full 3p sub-shell; potassium has one too many and chlorine one too few. If an electron is moved from one atom to the other, they each have a full sub-shell and achieve a condition of low energy. The atoms become the charged ions $K^+$ and $Cl^-$ and electrostatic attraction provides the force which holds the crystal together. As the ions approach each other the repulsive force between the full electron shells becomes important and the inter-atomic spacing in the resulting crystal corresponds to the distance at which these two electrostatic forces balance.

## 2.1.2 Covalent bonding

When atoms have three, four or five electrons in their outer shell, ionic bonding would involve the transfer of more than one electron from one atom to another. This would require a relatively large amount of energy and a different mechanism becomes important. In covalent bonding adjacent atoms share electrons to make up the required number. Consider the diamond form of carbon; the atom has the electronic configuration:

C    $1s^2$   $2s^2$   $2p^2$

i.e. it has four electrons in the second shell, which needs eight to be completely full. The carbon atom adopts a structure in which it has four nearest neighbours. It shares an electron with each of these and they, in turn,

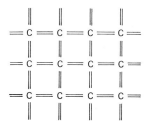

**Fig. 2.1**

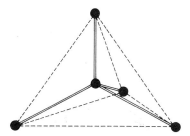

**Fig. 2.2** Tetrahedral bonding

also share electrons. It is convenient to think of these shared electrons as orbiting the two atoms although, bearing in mind the subtleties of quantum mechanics outlined in Chapter 1, this must be seen as no more than a simple model. Each atom now has part-ownership of eight electrons. The situation is shown in a two-dimensional representation in Fig. 2.1, in which each shared electron is indicated by a line joining the relevant two atoms.

Each bond consists of an 'electron cloud' of two electrons. There is considerable repulsive force between these clouds and the bonds therefore arrange themselves with the largest possible angle between them, which turns out to be 109.5°. Thus the four nearest-neighbour atoms are at the corners of a tetrahedron, as shown in Fig. 2.2. This gives rise to the diamond lattice structure, described in more detail later in the chapter.

### 2.1.3  Metallic bonding

In metals the outer electrons leave the atoms and are able to move about freely, not belonging to any particular ion. In copper, for example, one electron leaves each atom so that in a given piece of material the number of free electrons is equal to the number of atoms. The positive ions making up the crystal lattice are held together by the attraction of the surrounding negative cloud of electrons.

### 2.1.4  Van der Waals bonding

There are no 'spare' electrons in the case of the inert gases so it is clear that none of the preceding three mechanisms can operate. These gases do, nevertheless, solidify, albeit at very low temperatures. Similarly some molecules have no spare electrons because all bonds are satisfied within the molecule, e.g. $H_2$, $CO_2$, $CH_4$. It follows that there must be a bonding which works for atoms and molecules having full shells. This is Van der Waals bonding.

(a)                                                    (b)

**Fig. 2.3**  Van der Waals bonding

Any atom consists of positive and negative charges and the centres of gravity of these two sets of charge will not necessarily be at the same point in space. At any instant, therefore, an atom has a dipole moment, as shown in Fig. 2.3(a). The direction of the moment will vary rapidly, due to the motion of the electrons in the atom. When two atoms approach, the fluctuating moments affect each other and a lower energy configuration is achieved if they vary together, as shown in Fig. 2.3(b). This produces a net attractive force which can give rise to solidification. The force is nevertheless very weak and these solids have very low melting points.

## 2.2  Crystal structures

Most of the materials of interest to the electronics engineer solidify in crystalline form with fairly simple lattice structures. When they occur naturally, they are polycrystalline, i.e. a given piece consists of many small crystals, all oriented differently. They can be prepared in single crystal form, however, and almost all semiconductor applications require large single crystal specimens. In the case of silicon, for instance, single crystal boules in excess of a kilogram are routinely prepared in industry for processing into semiconductor devices.

### 2.2.1  Simple cubic and body-centred cubic structures

The unit structures for these two lattice types are shown in Fig. 2.4. The simple cubic lattice (Fig. 2.4(a)) has one atom at each corner of an imaginary cube. No element has this form, but ionic compounds like NaCl do, with alternate atoms Na and Cl, as indicated in the figure. Note that although eight atoms are shown, the number per unit cell is only one, since each atom belongs to eight adjacent units. The body-centred cubic (bcc) lattice is shown in Fig. 2.4(b); it has an extra atom in the centre of the cube. Iron and the alkali metals have this crystal structure.

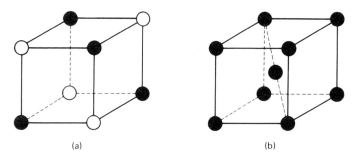

(a)                                    (b)

**Fig. 2.4**  (a) Simple cubic structure, (b) body-centred cubic (bcc) structure

### 2.2.2  Face-centred cubic and hexagonal close-packed structures

These two structures are dealt with together because they both come into the category of 'close-packed' structures. The basic cells are shown in Fig. 2.5. The face-centred cubic (fcc) lattice has an atom at each corner of the unit cube and one at the centre of each face; only six of these atoms are shown in Fig. 2.5(a) so as to make the diagram a little clearer. A number of metals, including aluminium, have this structure. The hexagonal close-packed (hcp) lattice is based on a hexagonal prism rather than a cube. Three layers of atoms are shown in Fig. 2.5(b); note that the atoms of layer III are vertically above those of layer I, but not those of layer II. Zinc, cadmium and cobalt have this structure.

Any crystal structure can be thought of as a series of two-dimensional layers stacked one on top of another and this concept is useful when considering close-packed structures. If a number of balls is arranged in a layer in such a

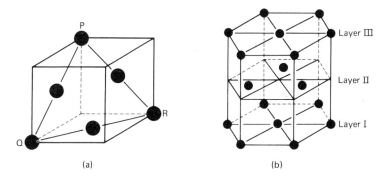

(a)                                    (b)

**Fig. 2.5**  (a) Face-centred cubic (fcc) structure, (b) hexagonal close-packed (hcp) structure

way as to occupy the minimum area, the arrangement shown in Fig. 2.6 is obtained. If layers of this type are arranged one on top of another, then the balls occupy the minimum possible volume. It is interesting, however, that the layers can be placed in more than one way. Consider three such layers and let the layer illustrated in Fig. 2.6 be the middle one, so that there is a layer below the plane of the diagram and one above it. The crosses and circles of the figure indicate the depressions where the balls of the adjacent layers will settle. Note that there are twice as many available depressions as balls in a layer. This means that the balls of an adjacent layer can either settle into the set of depressions marked by crosses or the set marked by circles. Suppose the balls below the layer of Fig. 2.6 settle into the crosses and the balls above settle into the circles. In this situation, none of the balls in the three layers is vertically above any other. If this stacking sequence of layers is repeated, the balls in the fourth layer will be vertically above those of the first and so on. The sequence is usually written ABCABCA... and gives rise to the fcc structure. This last

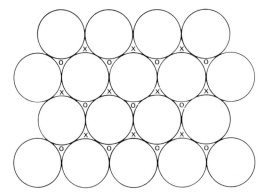

**Fig. 2.6** Close packing of spheres in two dimensions

assertion will not be immediately obvious to the reader and it is really necessary to study models to establish the point beyond any doubt. It should be noted, however, that the plane marked PQR in Fig. 2.5(a) is of the close-packed type and it is planes parallel to this one which have the ABC sequence, in fcc crystals.

If the balls both above and below the layer of Fig. 2.6 all settle into depressions of the same type, then a stacking sequence ABABA... is obtained, which gives the hcp lattice. This is a little more easy to see. Reference to Fig. 2.5(b) shows that the basal plane of the hexagon is close-packed and it has already been pointed out that balls in alternate layers are vertically above each other in this structure.

### 2.2.3  Diamond structure

Diamond is an important structure because a number of important semi-conductors, including silicon, crystallise in this manner. It is based on the tetrahedral bonding scheme of Fig. 2.2. When a number of these units are combined, the structure shown in Fig. 2.7 is obtained. The cell is basically

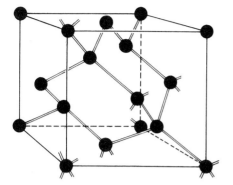

**Fig. 2.7** Diamond structure

cubic but is rather more complex than any discussed so far. One way of looking at it is to consider it as two identical inter-penetrating fcc lattices. If the first is based on a cube defined by the Cartesian co-ordinates $(0,0,0)$, $(1,0,0)$, $(0,1,0)$, $(0,0,1)$ etc., the second is based on the cube defined by $(\frac{1}{4},\frac{1}{4},\frac{1}{4})$, $(1\frac{1}{4},\frac{1}{4},\frac{1}{4})$, $(\frac{1}{4},1\frac{1}{4},\frac{1}{4})$, $(\frac{1}{4},\frac{1}{4},1\frac{1}{4})$ etc., i.e. the second cube is displaced from the first by a quarter of a body diagonal.

A number of compounds, such as the III-V semiconductors GaAs, GaP and InP, also have this structure and the lattice is then called zincblende rather than diamond. In these cases, adjacent atoms are different. This means that in GaAs, for instance, if the atom at the centre of the tetrahedron in Fig. 2.2 is gallium, the atoms at the corners are arsenic, and vice-versa. Once again the structure can be thought of as two inter-penetrating fcc lattices but one of them is now composed entirely of group III atoms and the other is made up of group V atoms.

## 2.3  Miller indices

It is obviously necessary to have a means of labelling planes and directions in crystal lattices. In the case of cubic crystals the method used is essentially the same as that employed in conventional vector algebra although the nomenclature is slightly different. Hexagonal crystals are slightly more awkward to deal with. We will consider cubic crystals first.

In Fig. 2.8 is shown a unit cube of side $a$. The plane which is to be labelled is shown shaded. The rules for determining Miller indices for planes are as follows. First set $x, y, z$ axes along the main cube directions and choose as the origin of axes a corner of the cube which is not in the plane concerned. The intercepts made by the plane on the $x, y, z$ axes are noted in units of the cube side ('$a$' in this case). The reciprocals of these three numbers are then taken and converted to the set of integers with the same ratio. In the case of the plane in Fig. 2.8 this gives:

| intercepts | $0.5a$ | $2a$ | $0.5a$ |
|---|---|---|---|
| reciprocals | 2 | 0.5 | 2 |
| integers | 4 | 1 | 4 |

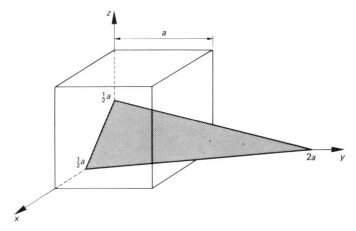

**Fig. 2.8** The (414) plane

It is described as the (414) plane. The use of round brackets here is important, since square brackets are used to indicate directions. When a plane intersects an axis at a negative value, a 'bar' notation is used; if the intersections had been $0.5a$, $-2a$, $0.5a$, for example, the plane would have been ($4\bar{1}4$). In practice the most important planes in a crystal are those with low-integer Miller indices since they are the ones which contain most atoms. In an extended crystal there will be many (414) planes, all parallel to the one shown. It is important to realise that a complete set of ($LMN$) planes would include every atom in the crystal.

It is convenient to group planes into families which are crystallographically the same. The three sides of the unit cube, for instance, are obviously of the same type, but have different sets of indices: (100), (010) and (001). These are referred to as the {100} family, the form of the brackets again being part of the notation. The four members of the {111} family are shown in Fig. 2.9. Using the axes shown, these are (111), ($11\bar{1}$), ($\bar{1}11$) and ($\bar{1}1\bar{1}$). The notation is not unique, however, as can be seen by moving the origins of axes to the points marked O′ in Figs 2.9(a) and 2.9(b), something we are quite at liberty to do. The four sets of Miller indices then become ($\bar{1}\bar{1}\bar{1}$), ($\bar{1}\bar{1}1$), ($1\bar{1}\bar{1}$) and ($1\bar{1}1$).

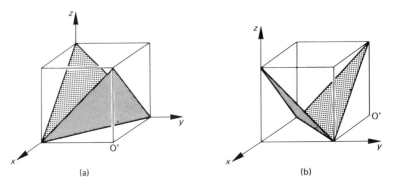

(a)

(b)

**Fig. 2.9** The {111} family of planes

Note that the second set of alternatives is the mirror image of the first, i.e. it is obtained by changing 1 to $\bar{1}$ and vice versa.

Directions in cubic crystals are indicated in a simple Cartesian manner, the origin of axes being taken as a corner of the unit cube through which the vector passes. The three indices are the $x$, $y$ and $z$ co-ordinates of the end of the vector, again multiplied by an appropriate factor to give three integers. No taking of reciprocals is involved. Two examples are given in Fig. 2.10. Note that square brackets are used and that changing the signs of the integers has the effect of reversing the direction of a vector. Again it is the low-integer indices which are the most important, since they correspond to the directions with the largest numbers of atoms. As with planes, directions can be grouped into families. The [100], [010], [001] directions, for instance, all represent cube edges and are called the $\langle 100 \rangle$ family in the Miller notation.

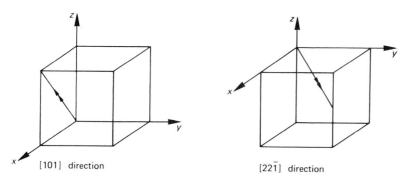

[101] direction          [22$\bar{1}$] direction

**Fig. 2.10**

Readers who have studied vector algebra may have noticed that the Miller indices for directions correspond to what the mathematician calls 'direction ratios'. This means that if we wish to determine angles between crystal directions, we can use directly the well-known rules for vectors. Suppose we wish to find the angle between the $[LMN]$ and $[L'M'N']$ directions. The direction ratios $L, M, N$ and $L', M', N'$ are first converted to 'direction cosines' $l, m, n$ and $l', m', n'$ as follows:

$$l = \frac{L}{\sqrt{L^2 + M^2 + N^2}}, \quad m = \frac{M}{\sqrt{L^2 + M^2 + N^2}} \text{ etc.} \tag{2.1}$$

The angle $\theta$ between the two directions is then given by

$$\cos\theta = ll' + mm' + nn' \tag{2.2}$$

In a cubic crystal, finding the angle between two planes is essentially the same problem as finding that between two directions. The direction $[LMN]$ is perpendicular to the plane $(LMN)$ so the angle between $(LMN)$ and $(L'M'N')$ is the same as that between $[LMN]$ and $[L'M'N']$. Some common sense must be exercised here, however, to allow for the fact that the crystallographer does not normally distinguish between the planes $(LMN)$ and $(\bar{L}\bar{M}\bar{N})$. If the above rules give the angle between $(LMN)$ and $(L'M'N')$ as

$\theta°$, then they will give the angle between $(\bar{L}\bar{M}\bar{N})$ and $(L'\,M'\,N')$ as $(180-\theta)°$. In the present context this should be regarded as essentially the same result.

## 2.4  Miller–Bravais indices

The system of Miller indices can be employed for hexagonal crystals, but it is inconvenient because there is not a 'natural' set of three perpendicular axes in the structure. It is more usual to employ three axes in the basal plane and one vertical axis, as shown in Fig. 2.11. The Miller–Bravais notation uses exactly the same rules as the Miller, but intercepts with the four axes in the order

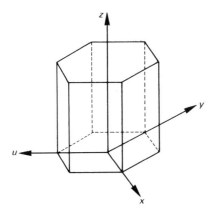

**Fig. 2.11**  Miller–Bravais axes

$x, y, u, z$ are now considered before taking reciprocals. This gives the basal plane the description (0001), for instance, and the vertical side planes (01$\bar{1}$0), ($\bar{1}$100), (10$\bar{1}$0) etc. It follows that there is some redundancy in the notation, since it must always be possible to describe a plane in a three-dimensional space by three numbers. It is left for the reader to satisfy himself that for any plane $(KLMN)$ the following equality must always hold

$$K + L + M = 0 \qquad (2.3)$$

## 2.5  Defects in crystals

The preceding sections have been concerned with the three-dimensional patterns formed by the various crystal lattices. A crystal with an atom at each lattice point is called 'perfect' and it is important to realise that such a thing does not occur in practice. This is not just because techniques of preparing crystals are less than ideal; the existence of the perfect crystal is actually forbidden by the laws of thermodynamics. The reason for this is interesting. Atoms solidify into fairly simple crystalline patterns because in this type of configuration they have the lowest possible energy and it is generally true that any system left to itself will move to the lowest energy configuration available to it. In addition to this force trying to create perfect order, however, there is another influence, namely thermal energy, which is trying to do the reverse, i.e. attempting to randomise the positions of the atoms. The thermal energy manifests itself as atomic vibrations of the atoms on the crystal lattice. At a given temperature the two influences find a balance and we have a crystal with a certain number of point defects, i.e. there are some lattice points which have no atoms and some atoms which occur at positions not corresponding to lattice points. These defects are referred to as vacancies and interstitials respectively. If the temperature is lowered, lattice vibration becomes less violent and the equilibrium concentrations of vacancies and interstitials are reduced. If, on the other hand, the temperature is raised then eventually the energy of the atomic vibrations overcomes the binding forces of the crystal and crystalline order is lost completely or, to put it another way, melting takes place.

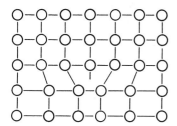

**Fig. 2.12** Edge dislocation

Vacancies and interstitials are not the only types of point defect which can occur, but a detailed consideration is beyond the scope of this book. From the point of view of semiconductor technology point defects are important because they can become charged and influence the electrical properties of the material. In certain cases the electrical properties of semiconductors are actually determined by the point defects.

In addition to the defects which are imposed on us by the laws of thermodynamics there are a number of others which commonly occur but which can, in principle, be eliminated. Foremost among these is the crystal boundary. As mentioned earlier, most crystalline materials occur naturally in the polycrystalline form, i.e. as many small crystals separated at their surfaces by crystal (or grain) boundaries. Grain boundaries are therefore best thought of as two-dimensional defects. Modern semiconductor technology is capable of producing large single crystals so, in practice, this defect causes few problems. More significant is the one-dimensional defect called the dislocation. The most important type as far as semiconductors are concerned is the edge dislocation, illustrated in Fig. 2.12. The defect is shown end-on in the diagram and can be considered as an extra half-plane of atoms forced into the crystal. This gives a line of atoms which, in the example shown, are bonded to three other atoms in the plane of the diagram, rather than four. A line of so-called 'dangling bonds' therefore exists along the length of the edge dislocation. These dangling bonds can act as traps for free electrons and can have a strong effect on the operation of any semiconductor device. The effect is usually for the worse and great efforts are made to eliminate dislocations from semiconductors. On the whole these efforts are fairly successful and it is claimed by commercial crystal growers that silicon, for instance, can be produced completely free of dislocations.

The study of dislocations has an importance which extends beyond the subject of semiconductor technology. It is because of the existence of these defects that metals are relatively weak and deform in a plastic manner. The strength of a perfect metal crystal would be some orders of magnitude greater than the strength found in real metals. The interested reader is referred to textbooks in physical metallurgy.

## 2.6 Problems

Problems marked * are considered in the computer package (see Preface).

**2.1*** How many atoms are there, per unit cube, in
(i) the simple cubic lattice?
(ii) the body-centred cubic lattice?
(iii) the face-centred cubic lattice?

**2.2*** A simple cubic lattice has sides 0.3 nm long. Calculate the
(i) angle between the [100] and [111] crystallographic directions,
(ii) angle between the normals to the (100) and (111) planes,
(iii) spacing between the (111) planes.

**2.3*** The smallest distance between any two atoms in a certain face-centred cubic crystal is 0.2 nm. Find the size of the unit cube and then calculate the lattice spacing for (100), (110), and (111) planes. Hence calculate the Bragg angles for second-order reflections from the (100), (110) and (111) planes when X-radiation of wavelength 0.07 nm is used.

**2.4*** An electron beam is accelerated through $V_1$ volts and is incident in a [100] direction on a face-centred cubic crystal of unit cube side 0.42 nm. Bragg diffraction is observed from the (111) planes. If the accelerating voltage is changed to $V_2$, then Bragg diffraction of the same order is obtained from the (101) planes. Calculate the ratio $V_1/V_2$.

**2.5** Calculate the angle of incidence for the first Bragg reflection from the (310) plane of a cubic crystal of lattice parameter 0.25 nm for X-rays of wavelength 0.07 nm. Show that no third-order reflections occur for this example.

**2.6** Explain the meaning of the term 'close-packed structure' in crystallography and draw a face-centred cubic crystal indicating clearly which are the close-packed planes.

If the distance between adjacent close-packed planes in a certain face-centred cubic structure is 0.23 nm, calculate the size of the unit cube for the crystal.

# 3 Conduction in Metals

It has been shown in the previous chapter that bonding occurs in a metal by electrons leaving individual atoms and forming a cloud within the confines of the crystal. These electrons are free to move and give rise to electrical conduction. The number of electrons involved depends on the element concerned; silver and gold, for instance, give one per atom, while zinc and cadmium give two each and aluminium gives three. In quantum-mechanical terms it can be said that each free electron belongs to all of the ions on the lattice, effectively forming part of an enormous 'molecule'. This gives rise to a set of discrete energy levels, as in the Bohr theory. Carrying the analogy further, we can see that the equivalent of the Bohr orbit is very large, since it is of the same dimensions as the crystal itself. Large orbits occur in Bohr theory for very large values of $n$ and for these values the energy levels are very close to each other. The same is true in metals, in fact the spacing is so small that the levels effectively form a continuum. The energy level scheme is indicated in Fig. 3.1.

Each of the energy levels is characterised by a set of three quantum numbers and, according to the Pauli principle, can hold only two electrons, one with clockwise spin and one with anti-clockwise spin. The free electrons therefore fill the levels, starting at the bottom, until all the electrons in the cloud are accommodated. If this filling-up process takes place at a temperature of 0 K, then the level at which it stops is called the Fermi level, so at 0 K all levels below the Fermi level contain electrons and all levels above it are empty. For temperatures above 0 K this statement is only approximately true,

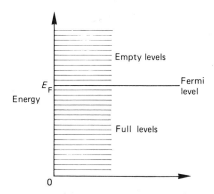

**Fig. 3.1** Energy levels in a metal

since a few electrons in states just below the Fermi level will be excited to states just above it. The '0 K' approximation is often found adequate for higher temperatures, however. For most metals the Fermi level energy, $E_F$, is a few eV above the bottom of the band of energy levels.

Although the levels of Fig. 3.1 are very close in terms of energy, they are not equally spaced; the levels get closer as the energy increases. The number of energy levels per unit volume of crystal within the energy range $E$ to $(E + dE)$ is $S(E)\,dE$, where $S(E)$ is called the density of states function. More

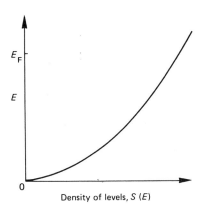

Density of levels, $S\ (E)$

**Fig. 3.2** Density of states function for a metal

will be written about this function in the following chapter on semiconductors, but for the moment it is sufficient to give its form as

$$S(E) = CE^{\frac{1}{2}} \tag{3.1}$$

where $C$ is a constant. The function is illustrated in Fig. 3.2. The fact that the density of energy levels increases with energy gives rise to the important result that the average energy of the free electrons is not very different to the Fermi energy. This can be seen as follows.

No. of electrons in range $E$ to $(E + dE) = CE^{\frac{1}{2}}dE$

Total energy of electrons in range $= (CE^{\frac{1}{2}}dE) \times E = CE^{\frac{3}{2}}dE$

Using the 0 K approximation, the electrons occupy levels between zero and $E_F$. The average energy, $\langle E \rangle$ is therefore given by

$$\langle E \rangle = \frac{\displaystyle\int_0^{E_F} CE^{\frac{3}{2}}dE}{\displaystyle\int_0^{E_F} CE^{\frac{1}{2}}dE} = \frac{3}{5}E_F \tag{3.2}$$

## 3.1 The electron gas model

This simple, but very useful, model treats electrons in a metal as particles in an empty box, the box corresponding to the metal crystal. They move about randomly with velocities ranging from zero to $v_F$, where $v_F$ is the velocity of an electron with the Fermi energy. Since the motion is random, any electron with velocity $v$ is balanced by another with $-v$. This must be so, otherwise there would be a net current flow without any applied voltage. The average velocity of the electrons turns out to be surprisingly large. Consider a metal with Fermi energy 5 eV. According to equation (3.2), the root mean square (rms) velocity, $v_R$, is given by

$$\frac{1}{2}mv_R^2 = \frac{3}{5} \times 5\,\text{eV} \tag{3.3}$$

A value for $v_R$ of the order of $10^6\,\text{m s}^{-1}$ is obtained.

At first sight this model would seem to be too simple. Not only does the 'box' in reality contain a lattice of atoms but these atoms are positively charged and must have a significant effect on the electrons. In fact, the model turns out to be fairly rigorous, if over-simplified. The quantum-mechanical solution predicts that if the electrons were in a perfect crystal, they would indeed hardly notice the existence of the lattice ions. (We will return to this point in Chapter 4 when effective mass is discussed.) However, it has been pointed out in Chapter 2 that the perfect crystal is not attainable. Defects such as foreign atoms, interstitials and vacancies disturb the ideal periodicity and cause scattering of the electrons. Much more serious in the case of metals, however, is the fact that the atoms do not stay fixed to the lattice points anyway. Thermal energy causes the atoms to vibrate at high frequency, and the higher the temperature, the greater the amplitude of vibration. Thus it is necessary to add to the model the concept of scattering of electrons by lattice vibrations or, to put it more simply, collisions between electrons and vibrating atoms.

In between collisions an electron moves in a straight line. At a collision it exchanges energy with the lattice and changes its velocity. Under steady state conditions, however, the distribution of velocities in the whole electron population does not change. As with a gas, a mean free time between collisions can be defined and also a mean free path. In copper at room temperature, for instance, the mean free path is about 40 nm, corresponding to about 200 atom spacings.

If a voltage is applied across the metal the electrons no longer travel in straight lines between collisions, but are accelerated in the direction of the electric field, following curved paths. The electrons acquire a drift velocity in the field direction which is superimposed on the normal random distribution of velocities. A net current therefore flows in the metal. Suppose the mean value of this drift velocity is $\langle v \rangle$. It is a simple matter to show that it is very small compared to the values of random velocity. Let a current of 100 mA flow

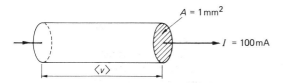

$A = 1\,\text{mm}^2$

$I = 100\,\text{mA}$

$\langle v \rangle$

**Fig. 3.3**

along a wire of cross-section 1 mm$^2$, as illustrated in Fig. 3.3. We need only consider the drift velocity of the electrons as the random velocities cancel each other out, by definition. Since this is only an order of magnitude calculation, it is quite in order to simplify matters a little by giving all electrons the average drift velocity $\langle v \rangle$ m s$^{-1}$. It follows from this that all the electrons within the cylinder of Fig. 3.3 will pass through the shaded surface in the course of one second. This amounts to $n \times \langle v \rangle \times A$ electrons, where $n$ is the numbr of electrons per unit volume. The current is therefore given by

$$I = -n \times \langle v \rangle \times A \times q \tag{3.4}$$

where the negative sign is a consequence of the negative charge of the electron. Substituting $I = 0.1$ A, $n = 10^{29}$ m$^{-3}$, $A = 10^{-6}$ m$^2$ a value of $6 \times 10^{-6}$ m s$^{-1}$ is obtained for $\langle v \rangle$. Although adequate to provide a measurable current, this is insignificant compared to the value of $v_R$ found from equation (3.3). It is therefore reasonable to assume that the values of mean free time between collisions and mean free path are unaffected by the application of an electric field.

## 3.2  Electron mobility and Ohm's law

In this section we use the above model to obtain an expression for electron mobility and hence derive Ohm's law. It is perhaps worth noting that the form of the law employed is not the familiar

$$V = IR \tag{3.5}$$

but

$$J = \sigma E \tag{3.6}$$

where $J$ is current density (A m$^{-2}$), $\sigma$ is conductivity ($\Omega^{-1}$ m$^{-1}$) and $E$ is electric field (V m$^{-1}$). It is left as an exercise for the reader to show the equivalence of the two expressions.

Consider unit volume of a metal, containing $n$ electrons. Let the total momentum of the electrons in the $x$-direction be $p_x$. In the absence of a field, $p_x$ is zero because of the random nature of the motion. Now apply an electric field $E_x$ in the $x$-direction. The electrons will experience a force in the negative $x$-direction and, from Newton's law,

$$\left( \frac{\mathrm{d}p_x}{\mathrm{d}t} \right)_{\text{field}} = -nqE_x \tag{3.7}$$

This cannot be the whole story, since the equation predicts a steady increase in electron momentum which, in turn, predicts a steady increase in current for constant field. An opposing frictional force must exist, therefore, and this is supplied by collisions between the electrons and the crystal lattice. The electrons are continually giving up momentum to the lattice and hence increasing its energy; this is the origin of Joule heating.

We assume that when an electron collides with the lattice it loses all of the energy it has acquired from the field and that its velocity after a collision is random, i.e. it is independent of the direction of motion before the collision. Suppose the probability of an electron undergoing collision during the time interval $dt$ is $dt/\tau$, where $\tau$ is defined as the relaxation time for the process. The same expression must also correspond to the fraction of electrons colliding during $dt$, so the net change in momentum in the x-direction during $dt$ is given by

$$dp_x = -p_x \frac{dt}{\tau} \tag{3.8}$$

i.e. the rate of loss of momentum due to the 'frictional' effect is

$$\left(\frac{dp_x}{dt}\right)_{\text{collisions}} = -\frac{p_x}{\tau} \tag{3.9}$$

Under steady state conditions the two effects must cancel, with no net change in momentum

$$\frac{dp_x}{dt} = \left(\frac{dp_x}{dt}\right)_{\text{field}} + \left(\frac{dp_x}{dt}\right)_{\text{collisions}} = 0 \tag{3.10}$$

which, using equations (3.7) and (3.9), comes to

$$-nqE_x - \frac{p_x}{\tau} = 0 \tag{3.11}$$

Since $p_x$ is defined as the momentum of the whole population of electrons in the x-direction,

$$p_x = nm \langle v_x \rangle \tag{3.12}$$

where $\langle v_x \rangle$ is the mean velocity of the electrons in the x-direction and $m$ is electron mass.

Substituting equation (3.12) into (3.11) gives an expression for $\langle v_x \rangle$

$$\langle v_x \rangle = -\frac{q\tau}{m} E_x \tag{3.13}$$

i.e. the mean drift velocity in the direction of an applied field is proportional to the magnitude of that field. The constant of proportionality is called the mobility, $\mu_n$:

$$\mu = \frac{q\tau}{m} \tag{3.14}$$

From equation (3.4) an expression for current density in the field direction, $J_x$, can be deduced

$$J_x = -nq \langle v_x \rangle$$

which, using equation (3.13), becomes

$$J_x = \frac{nq^2\tau}{m} E_x \tag{3.15}$$

which is Ohm's law for the specified field direction. Hence conductivity,

$$\sigma = \frac{1}{\rho} = \frac{nq^2\tau}{m} \tag{3.16}$$

where $\rho$ is resistivity.

A more useful form of equation (3.16), expressing it in terms of $\mu$, from equation (3.14), is

$$\sigma = ne\mu \tag{3.17}$$

## 3.3  Physical significance of $\tau$

The relaxation time, $\tau$, has appeared in the calculations as a probability term. It will now be shown that it corresponds to the mean free time between collisions. Consider the population of $n$ electrons in unit volume at $t = 0$ and let us keep looking at these electrons and watch them as they undergo their initial collisions. After time $t$ has elapsed a number $N(t)$ will still be uncollided. It has already been stated in Section 3.2 that the fraction undergoing collision in time $dt$ is $dt/\tau$ so the number colliding between $t$ and $(t + dt)$ is given by

$$dN(t) = -N(t) \cdot \frac{dt}{\tau} \tag{3.18}$$

where the negative sign indicates that $N(t)$ is decreasing with time. It follows that

$$\frac{dN}{dt} = -\frac{N(t)}{\tau} \tag{3.19}$$

At $t - 0$, $N(t) = n$, so the solution of equation (3.19) is

$$N(t) = n \exp\left(-\frac{t}{\tau}\right) \tag{3.20}$$

From equation (3.18) it can be deduced that a number of electrons $N(t) \cdot dt/\tau$ have a 'lifetime' of $t$. The mean time to collision is therefore

$$t_{mean} = \frac{1}{n}\int_0^\infty \frac{t \cdot N(t)}{\tau} dt$$

which, using equation (3.20), becomes

$$t_{mean} = \int_0^\infty \frac{t}{\tau} \exp\left(-\frac{t}{\tau}\right) \cdot dt = \tau \tag{3.21}$$

Equation (3.16) can now be used to obtain an order of magnitude estimate for the mean free time. Conductivity in metals is usually in the range $10^7$–$10^8$ $\Omega^{-1}$ m$^{-1}$ and $n$ is approximately $10^{29}$ m$^{-3}$. This gives to $\tau$ a value of about $10^{-14}$ seconds.

Having found the mean time between collisions, much the same method can be used to determine the mean square time between collisions. This is given by

$$t_{rms}^2 = \frac{1}{n}\int_0^\infty \frac{t^2 \cdot N(t)}{\tau}\,dt = 2\tau^2 \qquad (3.22)$$

i.e. $t_{rms} = \sqrt{2}\,t_{mean}$.

From equation (3.13) we see that the mean drift velocity is proportional to the mean time between collisions. Similarly, the rms velocity is proportional to the rms time between collisions, i.e.

$$\langle v^2 \rangle^{\frac{1}{2}} = -\frac{\sqrt{2}q\tau}{m}E_x \qquad (3.23)$$

This expression will be used in Section 3.5.

## 3.4 Temperature dependence of resistivity

We now give a simple derivation of the well-known result that resistivity in metals is proportional to temperature. The expression for conductivity is given in equation (3.16) and resistivity is simply the inverse. The number of electrons per unit volume is not a function of temperature in a metal and so it follows that any variation of resistivity with temperature must be due to changes in mean free time, $\tau$. Let us first consider why $\tau$ should be temperature-sensitive.

Collisions between electrons and the lattice occur because of atomic vibrations. We assume that the vibrations are random and constantly changing in direction so that over a short period of time an atom sweeps out a sphere in space, radius $r$, say. This sphere is the 'target' seen by the moving electron. It is illustrated in Fig. 3.4. It seems reasonable to assume that the probability of collision depends on the size of the sphere.

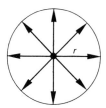

**Fig. 3.4** 'Disc' seen by electron approaching an atom

Suppose that at some instant the atom is vibrating along the $x$-axis, and assume that it moves with the simplest type of oscillatory motion, namely simple harmonic motion. The displacement in the $x$-direction is given by

$$x = r\sin 2\pi ft \tag{3.24}$$

where $f$ is the frequency of the oscillation. The kinetic energy of the motion is

$$\frac{M}{2}\left(\frac{dx}{dt}\right)^2 = \frac{M}{2}(4\pi^2 f^2 r^2 \cos^2 2\pi ft) \tag{3.25}$$

where $M$ is the mass of the atom. At $t = 0$, when the atom is in its central position, the kinetic energy is equal to the total energy of the particle, $E$, so

$$E = 2\pi^2 f^2 M r^2 \tag{3.26}$$

Elementary kinetic theory tells us that the energy of an atom at absolute temperature $T$ is given by

$$E = \frac{3}{2}kT \tag{3.27}$$

Comparison of equations (3.26) and (3.27) shows that $r^2 \propto T$. An electron approaching the vibrating atom will see a disc of area $\pi r^2$. It follows that the area of the target is proportional to the absolute temperature. Since by postulate the probability of collision, $P$, depends on the size of the target, we have

$$P \propto T \tag{3.28}$$

It has already been noted in Section 3.3 that the probability of a collision occurring is inversely proportional to $\tau$ (this was the original definition of $\tau$, in fact). This gives

$$T \propto \frac{1}{\tau} \tag{3.29}$$

Comparison of equations (3.29) and (3.16) gives the required relationship between resistivity and temperature:

$$\rho \propto T. \tag{3.30}$$

## 3.5  Joule heating

In this section we show that when a current passes through a metal a heating effect is observed proportional to the square of the current.

Since we have $n$ electrons per unit volume and the mean time to collision is $\tau$, the number of collisions per second per unit volume is given by $n/\tau$. On the average the amount of energy given to the lattice by a collision is $\langle \frac{1}{2}mv_x^2 \rangle$, where it is again assumed that the field is applied in the $x$-direction. Let the energy given to the lattice per second per unit volume be $W$. Then

$$W = \frac{n}{\tau}\langle \tfrac{1}{2}mv_x^2 \rangle \tag{3.31}$$

$$= \frac{nm}{2\tau}\langle v_x^2 \rangle \tag{3.32}$$

Substituting from equation (3.23)

$$W = \frac{nq^2\tau}{m}E_x^2$$

which from equation (3.16) can be written

$$W = \sigma E_x^2 \tag{3.32}$$

or, using Ohm's law,

$$W = \frac{J_x^2}{\sigma} \tag{3.33}$$

Equations (3.32) and (3.33) are alternative ways of expressing the formula for Joule heating.

## 3.6 Effect of defects on resistivity

So far we have only considered scattering of electrons by lattice vibrations. We now consider the effect of defects such as vacancies, interstitials and impurity atoms. A defect represents an interruption in the periodicity of the perfect lattice and the electric field in the vicinity is different to that close to a host atom. This interruption leads to a scattering of the electrons which is quite independent of the lattice vibrations and which depends almost entirely on the concentration of the defect concerned. If two (or more) scattering mechanisms exist in a crystal the collision probabilities are additive. Relaxation time, $\tau$, is inversely proportional to collision probability, so the value of $\tau$ for two processes, for instance, is given by

$$\frac{1}{\tau} = \frac{1}{\tau_d} + \frac{1}{\tau_l} \tag{3.34}$$

where $\tau_d$ is the relaxation time for scattering by some defect and $\tau_l$ is that for lattice scattering, as considered in previous sections. Since mobility $\mu$ is proportional to $\tau$, we can also write

$$\frac{1}{\mu} = \frac{1}{\mu_d} + \frac{1}{\mu_l} \tag{3.35}$$

At temperatures in excess of about 50 K, scattering by lattice vibrations predominates and resistivity is proportional to temperature, as indicated by equation (3.30). As the temperature is reduced, the vibrations become weaker and defect scattering becomes the main component of resistivity. Since this latter component is independent of temperature, the resistivity tends to a constant value, i.e.

$$\rho = \rho_d(c) + \rho_i(T) \tag{3.36}$$

where $c$ is the concentration of the defect concerned. Equation (3.36) is often called Matthiessen's rule; the variation of resistivity with temperature is indicated in Fig. 3.5.

For semiconductors, defects can have a major influence on mobility and resistivity even when they are measured at room temperature. This is especially true if the defects concerned are impurity atoms of a different valence to the host crystal. In the case of silicon, for instance, the electron mobility can be halved by the addition of group V atoms at a concentration in the region of $10^{23}$ m$^{-3}$. In semiconductor laboratories it is common for the 77 K mobility to be used as a figure of merit for the quality of a crystal.

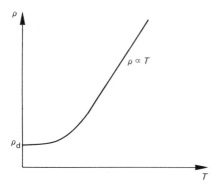

**Fig. 3.5**  Resistivity as a function of temperature

## 3.7 Problems

**3.1**   Given that the density of copper is $8.93 \times 10^3$ kg m$^{-3}$, calculate the
     (i)  number of free electrons per cubic metre,
     (ii) drift velocity when a current of density $10^4$ A m$^{-2}$ is flowing.

**3.2**   Given that the Fermi energy for a metal is about 1 eV above the bottom of the conduction band, show that the thermal velocity of electrons in a metal is very large compared to the drift velocity due to an electric field. (Assume a reasonable value for the concentration of electrons in the conduction band— this is an order of magnitude calculation.)

The drift velocity, $v$, is related to the mean time between collisions, $\tau$, by

$$v = \frac{qE\tau}{m}$$

where $q$ is electronic charge, $m$ is mass of an electron, and $E$ is the applied electric field. If the resistivity of a metal is typically $10^{-8}$ $\Omega$m, show that $\tau$ is of the order of $10^{-14}$ s.

**3.3**    Copper (relative atomic mass 64.5) has a density of $8.9 \times 10^3$ kg m$^{-3}$ and a resistivity of $1.8 \times 10^{-8}$ $\Omega$m. Silver (relative atomic mass 107.9) has a density of $10.5 \times 10^3$ kg m$^{-3}$ and a resistivity of $1.6 \times 10^{-8}$ $\Omega$m. Calculate the mean free time between electron collisions for these two metals.

# 4 Semiconductors

The theory outlined in the previous chapter is capable of accounting for a wide range of phenomena in metals but is not up to explaining some of the subtleties to be found when studying semiconductors. In the present chapter we discuss the Band Theory of solids and show that the content of Chapter 3 can be considered as a special case of this theory. We then go on to consider what determines the electrical conductivity of a semiconductor and finally describe the techniques which are used to measure it.

## 4.1 Band theory of solids

Consider the lithium atom labelled A in Fig. 4.1. The energy level scheme is also shown in the figure and it is clear that in the ground state the atom has two electrons in the 1s state and one in the 2s state. A second lithium atom a long way from atom A has an identical energy level scheme. Now consider what happens when the two atoms approach each other as in Fig. 4.2. The electrons on atom A are now subjected to a number of new forces, namely those of repulsion from the electrons of atom B and of attraction towards the nucleus of atom B. Similarly the electrons on atom B are in the potential field of the electrons and nucleus of atom A. All this has an effect on the energy level scheme (Fig. 4.2). The levels are split into two, one each side of the original level and the pairs of levels now belong to the two atoms. Since the splitting of the levels, $\Delta E$, is a consequence of the approach of the two atoms, its magnitude increases as the atoms get closer. The splitting of a 2s level is greater than that for a 1s level since the average distance of an electron from its nucleus is greater for $n = 2$ than for $n = 1$ and a 2s electron therefore intrudes further into the field of the other atom.

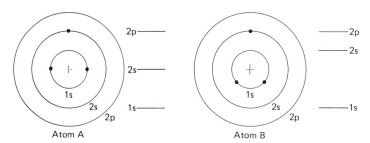

**Fig. 4.1** Energy level schemes for two isolated Li atoms

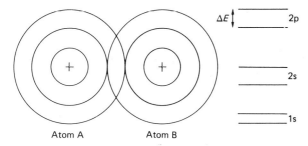

**Fig. 4.2** Energy level scheme for two adjacent Li atoms

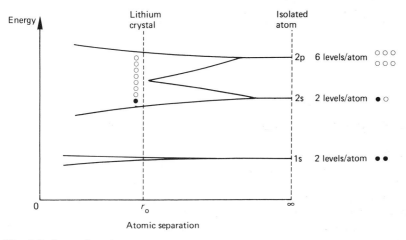

**Fig. 4.3** Formation of energy bands in Li

All this remains true for a much larger number of atoms. If, for instance, $10^{24}$ atoms are brought together to form a crystal there will be $10^{24}$ energy levels within the range $\Delta E$. The crystal then has 1s, 2s, 2p . . . bands, each containing this number of levels, separated by bands containing no levels at all, called 'forbidden gaps'. The variation in $\Delta E$ for the bands as the atoms get closer is shown in Fig. 4.3, again for lithium. The discrete levels broaden and eventually the 2s and 2p bands overlap to form a single 2s2p band with eight levels for every atom in the crystal.

We are usually only interested in the structure at the interatomic spacing corresponding to the crystal structure, i.e. $r_0$. It is usual to draw a section through the energy-separation diagram at this value and the resulting band diagram for lithium is shown in Fig. 4.4. Reference to Fig. 4.3 shows that at 0 K the lower band will be completely full and the upper band will be one-eighth full. By convention the highest band which is completely full at 0 K is called the 'valence band' and the one above that is called the 'conduction band'.

It should be noted that since lithium is a metal there must be some corres- pondence between the Band Theory as outlined here and the electron gas theory for metals given in the previous chapter. The electrons in the conduc- tion band correspond to the 2s electrons in the atomic state and it is these electrons which make up the electron gas. The energy level diagram given in Fig. 3.1 is therefore a picture of the conduction band of a metal and the theory of Chapter 3 ignores all bands below this one. This is a simplification of the true state of affairs, but one which gives a good approximation for metals. It will be shown below that this simplification is not acceptable for semiconductors.

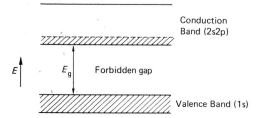

**Fig. 4.4** Energy band diagram for Li

## 4.2 Crystalline insulators and semiconductors

In the previous section it was shown that even at 0 K the conduction band of a metal contains some electrons and the material can therefore pass a current at this temperature. Some materials, namely semiconductors and insulators, have empty conduction bands at 0 K and this gives them a quite different set of characteristics. Consider the carbon atom which has atomic number 6 and the electronic signature $1s^2 2s^2 2p^2$ in the ground state. If a large number of carbon atoms is brought together to form a diamond crystal the energy levels broaden as in Fig. 4.5. The behaviour of the 2s and 2p levels is similar but not identical to the lithium case. The levels broaden and merge to form a single 2s2p band which is half-full. Further reduction in the inter-atomic spacing, however, causes a split between the upper four states and the lower four, and we again have two separate bands, one full and one empty. This is still the case at the

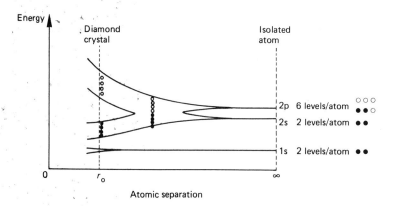

**Fig. 4.5** Formation of energy bands in diamond

separation $r_0$, corresponding to the diamond crystal. The 0 K energy band diagram therefore has a full valence band and an empty conduction band.

It is important to realise that neither a completely full band nor a completely empty band can give rise to an electric current. The second of these is obvious; if a conduction band contains no electrons there can be no electron flow and no current. The situation for a full band is less obvious, since there is clearly no lack of electrons. Suppose an electric field is applied to a diamond crystal at 0 K. In order for a current to flow some of the valence band electrons would have to be accelerated in the direction of the field. Since this involves an increase in energy they would have to move to higher energy levels within the band. This is not possible because there are no unoccupied energy levels to which they can move. It follows that a current cannot flow.

At temperatures greater than 0 K some valence band electrons can gain sufficient energy from lattice vibrations to make the jump into the conduction band. Conduction can then take place, since both bands are now partly full and can contribute to the flow of electric current. The extent to which this happens depends on the magnitude of the forbidden gap, $E_g$, relative to the amount of thermal energy available which is of the order of $kT$, where $k$ is Boltzmann's constant and $T$ is the absolute temperature. If $E_g$ is not too large a significant number of electrons can enter the conduction band and the material is called a semiconductor (most semiconductors have band-gaps in the region of 1 eV). If $E_g$ is large, the material is an insulator; diamond, for instance, has a band-gap of about 6 eV and is usually so classified. If the temperature is raised sufficiently, however, an insulator such as diamond has the characteristics of a semiconductor. Similarly, at very low temperatures all semiconductors are insulators.

The promotion of electrons across the forbidden gap can happen equally well in metals, of course (see Fig. 4.4). The number of extra electrons joining the conduction band in this way is always trivial compared to the number already there, however, and the effect can be neglected. The assumption underlying the theory of Chapter 3 that the concentration of free electrons in a metal is independent of temperature is therefore justified.

## 4.3  Electrons and holes

Using the convention of Fig. 2.1 a silicon crystal can be represented as in Fig. 4.6(a). Also shown, in Fig. 4.6(b), is the corresponding energy band representation. The figure is drawn for a temperature of 0 K with all electrons in valence orbits round silicon atoms, giving rise to a full valence band and an empty conduction band. If the temperature is increased, there is sufficient energy available to pull out some of these electrons from orbit, creating free conduction electrons. Fig. 4.7 illustrates this process using both the energy band model and the physical picture. Comparison of Figs 4.7(a) and 4.7(b) makes it clear why the lower band is called the valence band; the electrons it contains are those which form the valence bonds in the crystal. A clear physical meaning is also given to the band-gap energy $E_g$; it corresponds to the energy required to remove a valence electron from its orbit.

If a voltage is applied to the crystal the free electron will move towards the positive terminal. The valence electrons will also be attracted towards the

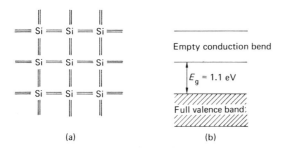

(a)                                    (b)

**Fig. 4.6** Silicon crystal: (a) physical picture, (b) band picture

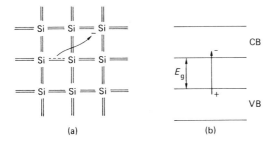

(a)                                    (b)

**Fig. 4.7** Creation of electron–hole pair

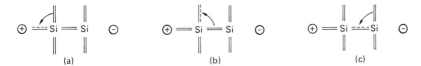

(a)                         (b)                         (c)

**Fig. 4.8** Movement of hole towards negative terminal

same terminal and will change their orbits in order to move in that direction. This has the effect of moving the 'empty bond' towards the negative terminal, as illustrated in Fig. 4.8. The 'empty bond' is called a hole and its motion through the crystal does constitute an electric current. The flow of current through a semiconductor therefore involves two entities, the electron and the hole, and in many respects it is convenient to consider the hole as a particle, effectively a positive electron.

Reference to Fig. 4.7(b) makes it clear that in a pure (or 'intrinsic') semiconductor the number of electrons in the conduction band is the same as the number of holes in the valence band, i.e.

$$n = p = n_i \tag{4.1}$$

where $n$ and $p$ are respectively the concentrations of electrons and holes (units: $m^{-3}$). The conductivity of the material is that due to electrons plus that due to holes. Equation (3.17) becomes

$$\sigma = \sigma_n + \sigma_p = nq\mu_n + pq\mu_p \tag{4.2}$$

where $\mu_n$, $\mu_p$ are the electron and hole mobilities (units: $m^2 V^{-1} s^{-1}$). For an intrinsic semiconductor, equation (4.2) becomes

$$\sigma_i = n_i q(\mu_n + \mu_p) \tag{4.3}$$

It must be emphasised that $n_i$ is rather a small number. In metals, for instance, the electron concentration is of the order of $10^{29} m^{-3}$. This should be compared to 300 K values of $n_i$ of $1.5 \times 10^{16} m^{-3}$ for silicon and $2.5 \times 10^{19} m^{-3}$ for germanium. It will be shown below that by doping a semiconductor the concentration of one of the carrier types can be increased, but it is unusual to find a semiconductor with more than about $10^{24}$ electrons or holes $m^{-3}$.

## 4.4 Effective mass

It has been mentioned in Chapter 3 that an electron travelling through a crystal under the influence of an externally applied field hardly notices the electrostatic field of the ions making up the lattice, i.e. it behaves as if the applied field were the only one present. This is the basis of the electron gas approximation and the assumption will now be looked at a little more closely.

If the electron were to experience only the applied field, $E$, then immediately after a collision it would accelerate in the direction of the field with an acceleration $a$, proportional to the applied force, i.e.

$$qE = ma \tag{4.4}$$

where the constant of proportionality is the electron mass, $m$. When quantum theory is applied to the problem of an electron moving through a crystal lattice, it predicts that under the action of an applied field the electron acceleration will indeed be proportional to the field, but that the constant of proportionality will be different from the normal mass of an electron:

$$qE = m_n a \tag{4.5}$$

The field due to the lattice ions can therefore be ignored providing we treat the electrons inside the crystal as if they had a slightly different mass to the real electron mass or, to put it another way, the effect of the lattice ions on an electron is to make it behave as if it had a different mass. This new mass is called the effective mass of the electron, $m_n$, and the effective mass of a hole, $m_p$ can be similarly defined. In general $m_n$ is different for different semiconductors and, in a given semiconductor, $m_n$ and $m_p$ are not the same. Usually $m_n$ is of the same order as $m$; in germanium, for instance, $m_n = 0.2 m$ and in silicon, $m_n = 0.4 m$.

The value of effective mass is an important parameter for any semiconductor, especially from the device point of view. Certain semiconductors, for instance, have low electron effective mass and hence high electron mobility. This makes them very suitable for high-frequency devices. The III-V semiconductor GaAs comes into this category and some of the best microwave transistors are made from this material.

## 4.5  Extrinsic semiconductors

The term 'extrinsic' is used to describe semiconductors which are doped with some impurity. For group IV semiconductors the most important dopants are those taken from groups III and V of the Periodic Table. We first consider group V impurities which give rise to n-type doping.

### 4.5.1  N-type semiconductors

Consider what happens when we replace a silicon atom inside a crystal with a phosphorus atom. Phosphorus has five electrons in its outer shell, so before putting it into the crystal we will remove one of these, creating a $P^+$ ion. The ion can then very easily assume much the same role in the crystal as that taken by the silicon atom which has been removed; it has four electrons to share with four nearest neighbours and each neighbour will in turn share one of its electrons so that a complete set of covalent bonds is formed. We are now left

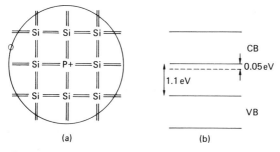

(a)                              (b)

**Fig. 4.9**  Addition of group V atom to Si

with the problem of putting in the fifth electron. What this last electron sees is a single positive charge embedded inside a silicon crystal. It therefore orbits it in much the same way as an electron orbits the nucleus of a hydrogen atom, as shown in Fig. 4.9(a). It is convenient to use Bohr Theory to analyse this situation, but two small modifications are necessary. First the effective mass of the electron must be used rather than the true electron mass and second the permittivity of silicon must be used rather than the permittivity of free space. Thus, using equation (1.5), the radius of the ground state orbit is given by

$$r = \frac{h^2 \epsilon_0 \epsilon_r}{\pi m_n q^2} \tag{4.6}$$

where $\epsilon_r$ is the relative permittivity of silicon, which is about 12 and $m_n$ is about $0.4\,m$. A value of 1.6 nm is obtained and this should be compared to the distance of 0.3 nm between atoms on the silicon lattice. It follows that the orbit of the fifth electron takes in a large number of atoms and it would be expected, therefore, that the binding energy of this electron would be less than that of a valence electron. This can easily be calculated using the formula for ionisation energy, equation (1.7), with the appropriate modifications:

$$E_1 = -\frac{m_n q^4}{8h^2 \epsilon_0^2 \epsilon_r^2} \tag{4.7}$$

This comes to 0.04 eV and gives the energy required to break the bond holding the fifth electron to its ion, i.e. to make it a free electron. This value should be compared with the band-gap energy of silicon (1.1 eV) which represents the energy required to free a valence electron. The ionisation energy for phosphorus in silicon can be measured experimentally and is found to be 0.05 eV. Bohr Theory therefore provides a simple and reasonably accurate model for the donor state.

When the fifth bond is broken the electron is free to conduct and is therefore in the conduction band. We say that the phosphorus atom has 'donated' an electron to the conduction band and the atom is called a 'donor'. Since the addition of 0.05 eV has been sufficient to raise the electron into the conduction band it follows that when orbiting the $P^+$ ion it must occupy a level 0.05 eV below the bottom of the band. These donor states are indicated as discrete levels in Fig. 4.9(b). Note that when an electron is excited into the conduction band in an intrinsic semiconductor two carriers are created, an electron and a hole. In an n-type semiconductor, only one carrier is made when a donor donates, namely an electron; the ion which is left behind is fixed in the lattice and cannot contribute to the current flow.

Because of the very small amount of energy required to ionise a donor atom, it is usual to assume that all donors have donated when calculating conductivity. Common sense must be used when applying this rule, however, since under certain circumstances it can give inaccurate results. If the temperature of the semiconductor is very low, for instance, the amount of thermal energy available is much reduced and some of the donors may remain unionised. Similarly, if the semiconductor has a very large concentration of donors the material starts to take on some of the characteristics of a metal and, once again, not all donors are ionised. However, if used with care the rule is both useful and simple; the point will be discussed further in Section 4.6 on semiconductor statistics.

The effect of adding the donors is greatly to increase the electron density, $n$, and hence to increase conductivity. The conductivity due to holes in an n-type semiconductor is negligible compared to that due to electrons so it can safely be ignored. It is instructive to calculate the conductivity of a doped semi-conductor and compare it with that of intrinsic material. Consider intrinsic silicon. The value of the intrinsic carrier concentration, $n_i$, is $1.6 \times 10^{16}$ m$^{-3}$ at room temperature, the electron mobility is 1.4 m$^2$ V$^{-1}$ s$^{-1}$ and the hole mobility is 0.5 m$^2$ V$^{-1}$ s$^{-1}$. Using these figures, equation (4.3) gives a value of $4.6 \times 10^{-3}$ $\Omega^{-1}$ m$^{-1}$ for $\sigma_i$. Now replace one silicon atom in $10^8$ with a group V donor. Silicon has about $5 \times 10^{28}$ atoms m$^{-3}$, so this means putting in a donor density, $N_D$, of $5 \times 10^{20}$ m$^{-3}$. If all donors donate, we have $n = N_D$ and, since hole conductivity can be ignored, the conductivity of the n-type semi-conductor is given by

$$\sigma = N_D q \mu_n \qquad (4.8)$$

which gives a value of $1.1 \times 10^2$ $\Omega^{-1}$ m$^{-1}$. This extreme sensitivity to minute amounts of dopant is one of the most important features of semiconductors. It also makes great demands on the semiconductor technologist; there is no point in deliberately adding one impurity in $10^8$ unless the material has been produced with a purity better than this.

### 4.5.2 P-type semiconductors

If an atom in a silicon crystal is replaced by a group III impurity then one bond is left unsatisfied. This is shown in Fig. 4.10(a) for the addition of a boron atom. It takes very little energy for an adjacent valence electron to move into this vacancy, as shown in the figure, and when this happens a hole is created. The energy band diagram for this process is shown in Fig. 4.10(b). The boron atom 'accepts' a valence electron and is therefore called an acceptor. When

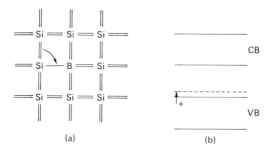

(a)                          (b)

**Fig. 4.10** Addition of group III atom to Si

the valence electron is transferred to the boron atom it is in an energy state just above the valence band. The boron atom becomes the ion $B^-$ and the hole is left in the valence band. The analogy with the situation for n-type material is obvious.

The effect of doping is again to increase the conductivity, but this time any current which flows is almost entirely due to the passage of holes. As before, it is usually safe to assume that all acceptors have accepted, so the concentration of holes, $p$, can be put equal to the concentration of acceptors, $N_A$. The conductivity is then given by

$$\sigma = N_A q \mu_p \tag{4.9}$$

### 4.5.3 Compensated semiconductors

If we add both donors and acceptors to a semiconductor the material can be either n- or p-type depending on which is added in greater concentration. Suppose we add $N_D$ donors m$^{-3}$ and $N_A$ acceptors m$^{-3}$ and let $N_D > N_A$. No energy is required for a donor to donate to an acceptor since this represents a downward transition on the energy diagram, as shown in Fig. 4.11. This

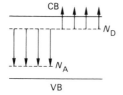

VB

**Fig. 4.11** Semiconductor containing both donors and acceptors

process happens preferentially, therefore. The remaining donors donate to the conduction band, as before, so the material is n-type with $n = N_D - N_A$. The important point to note is that if both donors and acceptors are added the effect is not additive; they tend to cancel each other out.

If $N_A > N_D$ the sample is p-type. If $N_A = N_D$ the material is similar to perfectly pure intrinsic material, with $n = p = n_i$. It is not identical, however, because the effect of electron and hole scattering at the impurity atoms is likely to reduce the electron and hole mobilities. In practice it would be extremely difficult to prepare this perfectly compensated material.

## 4.6 Semiconductor statistics

In order to calculate the electrical properties of semiconductors it is first necessary to find the electron and hole concentrations in the material. In this section we define the two important functions used and then give a fairly simple account of the method used to determine $n$ and $p$.

### 4.6.1 Density of states function

This function tells us how the energy levels (or 'states') are distributed within the allowed bands of energy. It is usually described as $S(E)$ and a form of this function has been given in equation (3.1) for the conduction band of a metal. This equation indicates that the number of states in a band increases with increasing energy as $E^{\frac{1}{2}}$. In an intrinsic semiconductor there are, by definition, no states in the forbidden gaps between the bands, so in these regions $S(E) = 0$.

In a semiconductor the number of states in a conduction band is always large compared to the number of electrons so in general we need only

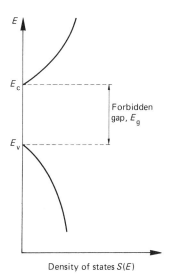

Density of states $S(E)$

**Fig. 4.12** Density of states function for a semiconductor

consider the form of $S(E)$ close to the bottom of the band, where the electrons are to be found. It can be shown that in this region $S(E)$ takes the form

$$S_c(E) = \frac{2^{\frac{5}{2}}m_n^{\frac{3}{2}}\pi}{h^3}(E - E_c)^{\frac{1}{2}} \tag{4.10}$$

where $E_c$ is the energy of the bottom of the conduction band. It can be seen that equation (4.10) is of the same form as equation (3.1). The number of holes in a valence band is small compared to the number of states and, since a hole represents the lack of an electron, it follows that the holes will float to the top of the band. We are therefore primarily interested in the form of a valence band near the top:

$$S_v(E) = \frac{2^{\frac{5}{2}}m_p^{\frac{3}{2}}\pi}{h^3}(E_v - E)^{\frac{1}{2}} \tag{4.11}$$

where $E_v$ is the top of the valence band. The form of these functions is given by Fig. 4.12, which should be compared to Fig. 3.2 in the chapter on metals. Note that

$$E_c - E_v = E_g \tag{4.12}$$

### 4.6.2 Probability function

It is not sufficient to know that an energy level exists. We also need to know whether or not it is occupied by an electron. The Fermi function, $F(E)$, gives the probability that a state at energy $E$ is occupied:

$$F(E) = \frac{1}{1 + \exp((E - E_F)/kT)} \tag{4.13}$$

where $E_F$ is the Fermi energy (or Fermi level), which was previously encountered in Chapter 3. Fig. 4.13 shows the form of the function for two temperatures, namely $T = 0$ K and $T > 0$ K. Note that since $F(E)$ is a probability it is confined to the range 0–1. At 0 K the function can have one of two values:

$$E > E_F, F(E) = 0$$
$$E < E_F, F(E) = 1$$

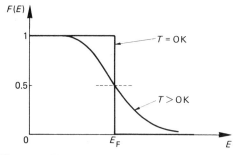

**Fig. 4.13** The Fermi function

Thus at 0 K all levels above the Fermi level are empty and all those below it are full. A metal has electrons in its conduction band at 0 K, so $E_F$ must be within that band, as in Fig. 4.14(a). A semiconductor, on the other hand, has a completely full valence band and an empty conduction band at 0 K so the Fermi level must be within the forbidden gap, as in Fig. 4.14(b). It will be shown below that at 0 K it is, in fact, at the mid-point of the gap in an intrinsic semiconductor.

For temperatures greater than absolute zero the step function smooths out and $E_F$ is best described as the energy at which the probability of occupation is $\frac{1}{2}$. Of course, there will only be electrons at energy $E_F$ if levels exist at this energy.

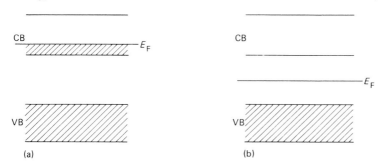

**Fig. 4.14**  Showing position of Fermi level at 0 K, (a) for a metal, (b) for a semiconductor

### 4.6.3  Density of electrons in the conduction band

Suppose a conduction band occupies the energy interval $E_c$ to $E_T$ and let the energy $E$ be within the band, i.e. $E_T > E > E_c$. Consider the range $E$ to $(E + dE)$. The number of states per unit volume within this range is $S_c(E)\,dE$, by definition of $S(E)$. The probability of occupation of these states is $F(E)$. The number of occupied states per unit volume is therefore given by $F(E)\,S_c(E)\,dE$. This corresponds to the concentration of electrons within $dE$, which is $dn$, where

$$dn = F(E)S_c(E)\,dE \tag{4.14}$$

Integrating this over the whole band, the total number of filled states becomes

$$n = \int_{E_c}^{E_T} F(E)S_c(E)\,dE \tag{4.15}$$

where $F(E)$ and $S_c(E)$ are given by equations (4.13) and (4.10).

Integration of equation (4.15) does not look difficult, but in fact it proves to be quite intractable and simplifications have to be made in order to get an analytic solution. If the exponential term in the denominator of equation (4.13) is large compared with unity, then an approximate expression is obtained:

$$F(E) \cong \exp\left(\frac{E_F - E}{kT}\right) \tag{4.16}$$

Since most of the electrons are known to occupy a small fraction of the energy levels at the bottom of the conduction band, the value taken for the top of the band, $E_T$, is not very significant and to a good approximation the upper limit of the integral in equation (4.15) can be taken as infinity. Inserting both of these approximations into (4.15) gives the expression

$$n = \frac{2^{\frac{1}{2}} m_n^{\frac{3}{2}} \pi}{h^3} \exp\left(\frac{E_F}{kT}\right) \int_{E_c}^{\infty} (E - E_c)^{\frac{1}{2}} \exp\left(-\frac{E}{kT}\right) dE \qquad (4.17)$$

This integration proves to be much more friendly. If the variable is changed to

$$x = \frac{E - E_c}{kT} \qquad (4.18)$$

equation (4.17) becomes

$$n = \frac{2^{\frac{1}{2}} m_n^{\frac{3}{2}} \pi (kT)^{\frac{3}{2}}}{h^3} \exp\left(\frac{E_F - E_c}{kT}\right) \int_0^{\infty} x^{\frac{1}{2}} e^{-x} dx \qquad (4.19)$$

The integral in equation (4.19) is standard and has the value $\frac{1}{2}\sqrt{\pi}$. The final expression for electron concentration is:

$$n = 2\left(\frac{2\pi m_n kT}{h^2}\right)^{\frac{3}{2}} \exp\left(\frac{E_F - E_c}{kT}\right) \qquad (4.20)$$

This expression is often written in the form

$$n = N_c \exp\left(\frac{E_F - E_c}{kT}\right) \qquad (4.21)$$

where $N_c$ is called the 'effective density of states'. This is a rather misleading description, since it certainly does not correspond to the total concentration of energy levels in the conduction band. The term is widely used, however.

It is now necessary to examine the simplifications that were made in deriving equation (4.20). The second of these, in which the top of the conduction band was put at $E = \infty$, instead of $E = E_T$, presents few problems. The function $F(E)$ decreases exponentially with increasing energy, so is zero at $E = \infty$. In practice the top of the band is sufficiently far above $E_c$ for $F(E)$ to be almost zero at $E = E_T$. The approximation is therefore a good one. The first of the approximations, on the other hand, is good only if

$$\exp\left(\frac{E - E_F}{kT}\right) \gg 1 \qquad (4.22)$$

This means that for all energies $E$ the relation $(E - E_F) \geq 3kT$ must hold. The lowest energy of interest here is $E_c$, the bottom of the conduction band. The approximation is therefore valid only if the Fermi level is more than about 3 $kT$ below the bottom of the conduction band. This will be the case more often than not, but in very highly doped material the Fermi level can approach the band and even enter it. Certain devices, including tunnel diodes and solid state lasers, are made from material of this kind. Some care must be exercised, therefore, when using equation (4.20), although very highly doped semiconductors will not be considered in detail in this book.

### 4.6.4  Density of holes in the valence band

Since the probability of a level at energy $E$ being occupied by an electron is $F(E)$, the probability of its being occupied by a hole is $1 - F(E)$. The number of holes per unit volume in the valence band is therefore given by

$$p = \int_{E_B}^{E_v} [1 - F(E)] S_v(E)\, dE \tag{4.23}$$

where $E_B$ is the bottom of the valence band and $S_v(E)$ is given by equation (4.11). A mathematical procedure entirely analogous to that for the conduction band, making essentially the same approximations, gives an expression for hole concentration, $p$

$$p = 2 \left( \frac{2\pi m_p kT}{h^2} \right)^{\frac{3}{2}} \exp \left( \frac{E_v - E_F}{kT} \right) \tag{4.24}$$

which is often written

$$p = N_v \exp \left( \frac{E_v - E_F}{kT} \right) \tag{4.25}$$

where $N_v$ is called the effective density of states in the valence band. The approximations used in the derivation mean that equation (4.24) is only valid if the Fermi level is several $kT$ above the top of the valence band.

### 4.6.5  Electron–hole product

The product of equations (4.21) and (4.25) is

$$np = N_c N_v \exp \left( -\frac{E_g}{kT} \right) \tag{4.26}$$

since $E_c - E_v = E_g$. The effective densities of states depend only on temperature, so equation (4.26) indicates that at constant temperature the product of electron and hole concentrations is a constant. This is a very important result. It means that if the electron concentration is increased by a factor of ten, say, by the addition of donors, then the concentration of holes is automatically reduced by the same factor. This justifies the assumption made in Section 4.5.1 that the conductivity due to holes is negligible in an n-type semiconductor.

For an intrinsic semiconductor $n = p = n_i$, so equation (4.26) becomes

$$n_i^2 = N_c N_v \exp \left( -\frac{E_g}{kT} \right) \tag{4.27}$$

Comparison of equations (4.26) and (4.27) gives

$$np = n_i^2$$

where $n_i$ depends only on temperature for a given semiconductor.

## 4.7 Position of the Fermi level

It is a simple matter to determine the position of the Fermi level for intrinsic material. In an intrinsic semiconductor, $n$ and $p$ are the same so equations (4.20) and (4.24) can be put equal to each other. If this is done, an expression for $E_F$ is found:

$$E_F = \frac{E_c + E_v}{2} - \frac{3}{4}kT\ln\left(\frac{m_n}{m_p}\right) \tag{4.29}$$

The first term corresponds to the middle of the forbidden gap. The second term is normally very small, since effective masses of electrons and holes in a given material are not usually very different and, in any case, it is only the logarithm of the ratio which appears. If $m_n = m_p$, the second term is zero and the Fermi level is exactly at the centre of the gap. Note that the same is true at the absolute zero of temperature.

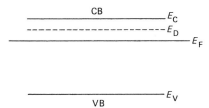

**Fig. 4.15**

If donors are added to the semiconductor, electrons enter the conduction band and $n$ increases. Inspection of equation (4.21) shows that the Fermi level must then be pulled up towards the conduction band (remember that $(E_F - E_c)$ is a negative quantity). As the Fermi level rises up the band, $p$ decreases by an amount given by equation (4.25). Similarly, if acceptors are added to the intrinsic semiconductor, $p$ increases and the Fermi level is dragged down towards the valence band. The simultaneous decrease in $n$ is now given by equation (4.21).

The occupation of donor and acceptor levels is also determined by the Fermi function and we are now in a position to examine the frequently-made assumption that all donors have donated and all acceptors have accepted. Suppose $N_D$ donors per unit volume are added to a semiconductor and let them give rise to energy levels at energy $E_D$ as in Fig. 4.15. The concentration of full donor states is given by $N_D F(E_D)$. These are the states which have not donated. We are more interested in the concentration of states which have donated; call this concentration $N_D^+$, since when a donor donates it becomes a positive ion.

$$N_D^+ = N_D - N_D F(E_D) \qquad (4.30)$$

which, substituting from equation (4.13), becomes

$$N_D^+ = N_D \left( \frac{\exp \left( \dfrac{E_D - E_F}{kT} \right)}{1 + \exp \left( \dfrac{E_D - E_F}{kT} \right)} \right) \qquad (4.31)$$

If all donors have donated, then $N_D^+ = N_D$. Equation (4.31) shows that the condition for this is

$$\exp \left( \frac{E_D - E_F}{kT} \right) \gg 1 \qquad (4.32)$$

i.e. the donor level must be several $kT$ above the Fermi level. Thus the assumption that all donors donate is acceptable providing the Fermi level is below the donor level and not too close to it. An equivalent argument for acceptors, which is left to the reader to derive, shows that it can be assumed that all acceptors have accepted providing the Fermi level stays more than about $3\,kT$ above the acceptor level.

If in the example shown in Fig. 4.15 we are not sure that the above assumption is valid, we cannot put $n = N_D$ and a slightly more involved procedure must be used to find $n$. In the semiconductor there are three species of charged particle: electrons, holes and ionised donors. Since the semiconductor as a whole must be neutral,

$$p + N_D^+ = n \qquad (4.33)$$

For the example of an n-type semiconductor, $p$ is so much smaller than the other two terms that it can be neglected and we have

$$N_D^+ = n \qquad (4.34)$$

If $N_D^+$ is substituted in equation (4.34), from (4.31), and $n$ is substituted from (4.20), an equation is obtained in which $E_F$ is the only unknown quantity. (It is probably most convenient in this calculation to take the origin of energy as $E_v$. If $E_v = 0$, then $E_c$ is numerically equal to $E_g$, the band-gap energy.)

Having found $E_F$, $n$ is calculated from equation (4.20) and, if required, $p$ can be found from equation (4.24).

## 4.8  The Hall effect

So far this chapter has been concerned with the calculation of electron and hole concentrations from the basic parameters of the semiconductor. In this section we consider the way in which $n$ and $p$ are measured in the laboratory. It is clear that a simple measurement of conductivity is not adequate, since it does not tell whether the current is carried by electrons or holes and a piece of n-type semiconductor looks remarkably like a piece of p-type. The extra piece of information is given by the Hall effect.

Consider the piece of semiconductor shown in Fig. 4.16. If a current is passed along the $x$-axis and a magnetic field $B_z$ is applied along the $z$-direction, a field, $E_y$, called the Hall field, is found to appear in the $y$-direction. The presence of the field can be detected by measuring a potential difference between faces 1 and 2. The direction of the Hall field depends on whether the

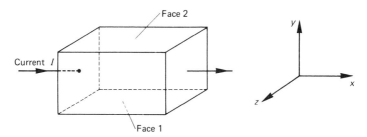

**Fig. 4.16**

current carriers are electrons or holes, so the measurement gives an immediate indication of whether the sample is n- or p-type. The concentration of the carriers can also be found and if a conductivity measurement is also carried out, the mobility of the majority carrier can be determined.

For a given sample it is found that the size of the Hall field is proportional to the current density, $J_x$, and the magnetic field, i.e.

$$E_y = RB_zJ_x \qquad (4.35)$$

where $R$ is called the Hall coefficient for the sample. Note that it is positive if the Hall field is in the positive $y$-direction.

Suppose the sample is p-type. The current in Fig. 4.16 is then carried by a flow of holes, velocity $v$, say, in the positive $x$-direction. As they cross the semiconductor the holes experience a transverse force $B_z\,qv$ due to the magnetic field. This force drives holes down on to face 1, as shown in Fig. 4.17 and the lower face of the semiconductor becomes positively charged, creating the Hall field in the $y$-direction. The Hall field exerts an upward force on holes

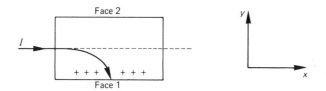

**Fig. 4.17**  Hall effect

passing through the crystal, equal to $qE_y$ and in the steady state the two forces just balance so no further increase occurs in the positive charge on face 1. In the steady state,

$$qE_y = B_z q V \qquad (4.36)$$

Modifying equation (3.4) for conduction by electrons, we have

$$J_x = pqv \qquad (4.37)$$

Using these two equations to substitute for $E_y$ and $J_x$ in equation (4.35),

$$R = \frac{1}{qp} \qquad (4.38)$$

So the magnitude of the Hall coefficient gives the hole concentration, $p$.

Now consider what happens if the sample being measured is n-type so that the current is due to electrons. In order for the current to pass in the positive $x$-direction, the electron flow must be in the negative $x$-direction. The force experienced by the electrons is in the same direction as the holes in the previous example, i.e. downwards, since in the expression $B_z q v$ both the sign of the charge and the sign of the velocity have changed. The bottom face of the sample becomes negatively charged and so the Hall field is this time in the negative $y$-direction. The quantity $E_y$ is therefore negative and, from equation (4.35), $R$ is also negative. Apart from these changes, the theory is the same as before and the concentration of electrons is given by

$$-R = \frac{1}{qn} \qquad (4.39)$$

Once we have performed a Hall measurement we know if the sample is n- or p-type and have a value for the majority carrier concentration. Suppose it turned out to be n-type. A measurement of conductivity gives $\sigma_n$, where

$$\sigma_n = nq\mu_n \qquad (4.40)$$

Since $n$ is known, electron mobility can be calculated. Similarly a combination of Hall and conductivity measurements on a p-type sample gives $p$ and $\mu_p$.

## 4.9 Problems

Problems marked * are considered in the computer package (see Preface).

**4.1** A 1 kg single crystal of silicon is grown containing 6 $\mu$g of the group V impurity phosphorus (relative atomic mass 30.97). A rectangular block is cut from the crystal with dimensions 15 mm, 4 mm and 3 mm in the $x$-, $y$- and $z$-directions, respectively. A magnetic field of 1.5 T is applied in the z-direction and a current of 30 mA is passed along the x-direction. Hall probes are connected to the centres of the narrow sides. Determine the following:

    (a) the sign and value of the Hall coefficient;
    (b) the Hall field (making sure that you indicate clearly the direction in which it acts);
    (c) the potential drop along the length of the specimen;
    (d) the voltage measured between the Hall probes.

**4.2**   A 0.1 kg ingot of germanium was doped during growth with a small quantity of the group III element gallium. Subsequent electrical measurements showed that the conductivity of the material was 15 $(\Omega m)^{-1}$. State whether the crystal was n-type or p-type and calculate the weight of gallium that had been added.

Suppose the same weight of antimony (group V) had also been added. Would the crystal then have been n- or p-type? What would have been the conductivity of this material?

[Assume all donors and acceptors are ionised].

**4.3**   Calculate the approximate free electron density and the approximate position of the Fermi level in samples of n-type germanium with resistivities of 0.02 $\Omega m$ and $2 \times 10^{-4}$ $\Omega m$ respectively, given that the temperature is 300 K, the electron mobility is 0.39 $m^2 V^{-1} s^{-1}$, and the 'effective' density of energy levels in the conduction band is $1.02 \times 10^{25}$ $m^{-3}$.

Calculate for p-type samples, with the same resistivities, the hole density and position of the Fermi level, given that the hole mobility is 0.19 $m^2 V^{-1} s^{-1}$ and the 'effective' density of energy levels in the valence band is $5.65 \times 10^{24}$ $m^{-3}$.

**4.4**   Assuming the 'effective density of states' in both the conduction and valence bands are $2.5 \times 10^{25}$ $m^{-3}$ and are independent of temperature, calculate the free electron densities in intrinsic germanium and silicon at 300 K, 350 K and 400 K.

By assuming that the mobility is constant, and the forbidden energy gaps and intrinsic resistivities of germanium and silicon at 300 K are as follows:

|  | Forbidden Energy Gap (eV) | Intrinsic Resistivity ($\Omega m$) |
|---|---|---|
| Germanium | 0.7 | 0.47 |
| Silicon | 1.15 | 2000 |

calculate the resistivities at 350 K and 400 K.

**4.5***   The following three ingots of germanium were prepared:

    (i) 100 g of germanium and 3.22 $\mu$g of antimony,
    (ii) 100 g of germanium and 0.73 $\mu$g of gallium,
    (iii) 100 g of germanium, 3.22 $\mu$g of antimony and 0.73 $\mu$g of gallium.

The relative atomic masses of gallium and antimony are respectively 69.72 and 121.76. If the density of germanium is 5460 kg $m^{-3}$, and the electron and hole mobilities are respectively 0.39 $m^2 V^{-1} s^{-1}$ and 0.19 $m^2 V^{-1} s^{-1}$, calculate the charge carrier density and the conductivity of all three samples.

**4.6**   An ingot of germanium is formed from a melt containing 100 g of germanium and 5.0 $\mu$g of indium (relative atomic mass 114.76). A specimen with dimensions, 2 cm $\times$ 1 mm $\times$ 1 mm, is cut from the ingot; calculate its resistance before and after exposure to a flash of light containing $1.8 \times 10^{13}$ photons, assuming that each photon produces an electron–hole pair. Use the hole and electron mobilities given in Appendix 2.

**4.7***   A silicon crystal is made n-type by introducing $N_D$ donor levels per m$^3$. The donor energy level and the Fermi level, $E_F$, coincide at 0.1 eV below the bottom of the conduction band, $E_C$. Calculate the electron, hole and donor densities for the crystal.

Sufficient acceptors, $N_A$ m$^{-3}$, are now added to make $E_F$ drop to 0.2 eV below $E_C$. Calculate $N_A$.

Assume a temperature of 300 K and take the effective masses of electrons and holes to be 1.1 $m_0$ and 0.59 $m_0$, respectively. The band-gap of silicon is 1.11 eV.

**4.8**   Explain how the Bohr theory of the hydrogen atom can be modified to provide a simple model for a donor atom in a semiconductor. Hence calculate the ionisation energy for a group V impurity in germanium and give an estimate for the mean distance of the electron from the ion when the donor level is occupied.

# 5 The p–n Junction

Having studied p-type and n-type semiconductors in some detail, we are now in a position to consider the properties of a sample which is partly n-type and partly p-type. The junction between the n- and p-type portions turns out to have special properties which form the basis of many devices. Let it be said straight away that it is not possible to make a junction by mechanically pressing together an n-type and a p-type sample. In practice a homogeneous sample is subjected to a diffusion treatment to introduce a relatively high density of impurities of the opposite type into a region of the crystal. Thus if we start with an n-type sample, the diffusion introduces sufficient acceptors to turn part of it p-type. A junction appears between the diffused p-type portion and the original n-type. It is convenient, however, from the point of view of explaining the action of the junction, to pretend that it is possible to form a p-n junction by pushing together a piece of p-type and a piece of n-type semiconductor. This fiction will be maintained in what follows.

## 5.1 Qualitative approach

Fig. 5.1(a) shows the two samples before they are joined. Both are electrically neutral at this stage. The p-sample contains many holes which can move about freely and a roughly equal number of ionised acceptors, which cannot. It also contains a relatively minute number of electrons. Similarly, the n-specimen contains mobile electrons, immobile ionised donors, and very few holes. Now form the junction by joining the two samples, as in Fig. 5.1(b). A junction of this sort is called an abrupt junction because of the sudden change from p- to n-type at the junction.

Consider first the instantaneous movement of holes. Because they move about randomly, some leave the n-portion and enter the p-portion, and some do the reverse. The concentration in the p-side is enormous compared to that on the n-side, however, so the initial hole current p→n is very much greater than that going n→p. The instantaneous effect of joining the two samples, therefore, is for a net hole diffusion current to flow left–right across the junction. The holes penetrating into the n-side eventually meet up with electrons and recombine with them. Left behind on the p-side are uncompensated ionised acceptors; a region of negative charge therefore builds up at the junction on the p-side.

An exactly analogous situation occurs for electrons. A net diffusion of electrons takes place, right–left across the junction. A positive space-charge builds up at the junction due to the presence of the ionised donors which have

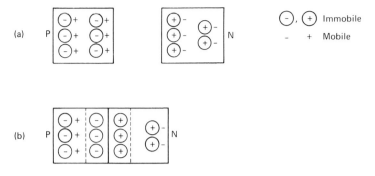

**Fig. 5.1** (a) p- and n-type samples before joining, (b) same samples after joining to form a p–n junction

been abandoned by their electrons. The picture is shown in Fig. 5.1(b), in which the specimen has two space-charge regions facing each other at the junction, one negative and the other positive. Because the whole sample must be electrically neutral (it is, after all, made up from two specimens that were both neutral), those regions must contain equal and opposite amounts of charge. The region of space-charge is often called the 'depletion region' because it is depleted of electrons and holes.

The foregoing gives the instantaneous effect of joining the two original specimens. This state of affairs does not last long, however, for the following reason. The space-charges at the junction give rise to an electric field in the depletion region. Consider the effect of this field on the movement of holes. The sense of the field is such as to assist the (very small) hole flow from n to p, but to oppose, and severely reduce, the initial large flow of holes from p to n. A steady state quickly builds up in which the electric field is just large enough to reduce the flow of holes going p→n to that going n→p. To put it another way, the large initial flow of holes from p to n brings about its own reduction because it causes the field to build up in the depletion region.

Exactly the same is true for electrons. The initial high flow of electrons from the n-side to the p-side is quickly reduced by the setting up of the electric field. In the steady state, the reduced value is equal to the very small flow of electrons from p to n. It must be realised that this steady state would come about very quickly, and what has taken several paragraphs to describe would occur, to all intents and purposes, immediately.

It follows that at equilibrium, with no external voltage applied to the junction, four separate currents flow across. There are equal currents of holes flowing in each direction and, similarly, equal currents of electrons. There is thus no net current across the junction, as common sense demands. In general the hole currents are different in magnitude from the electron currents.

## 5.2 Band-theory approach

In a previous chapter we have seen how to represent p-type and n-type semiconductors using the concept of energy bands. We can now apply the same ideas to the p-n junction. Let us pursue the same 'thought-experiment' that was described in the previous section, i.e. start with two separate pieces of semiconductor, one n-type and the other p-type, and push them together to form a junction.

Fig. 5.2(a) shows the situation when the two pieces are separate. The p-type piece has its Fermi level close to the valence band, and the n-type has it close to the conduction band. Also shown in the diagram is the Fermi level when the semiconductor is in its intrinsic state. This is at the middle of the band-gap to a good degree of accuracy. (In fact, it is exactly at the middle if the effective

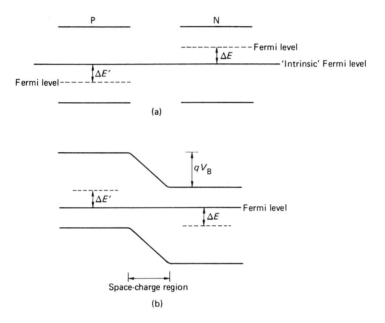

**Fig. 5.2** (a) Band diagram corresponding to Fig. 5.1(a), (b) band diagram corresponding to Fig. 5.1(b)

masses of electrons and holes for the semiconductor are equal.) The width of the forbidden gap and the 'intrinsic' position of the Fermi level are the same for both specimens since the two pieces are assumed to be of the same material. The actual Fermi levels are removed in energy respectively $\Delta E'$ and $\Delta E$ from the 'intrinsic' level.

Now join the two pieces together, forming a p-n junction. It has been noted in the previous section that a space-charge region develops at the junction giving rise to an electric field. This field is such as to assist the flow of electrons from p to n, i.e. the n-type must be at a lower electron potential energy than the p-type. The bands on the n-side must therefore move down the energy axis compared to the bands on the p-side, as shown in Fig. 5.2(b). A potential energy barrier, height $qV_B$, develops at the junction, caused by the electric field.

As stated above, the equilibrium value of $qV_B$ is that value which just equalises the flow of carriers in the two directions, across the junction. It can be shown by a thermodynamic argument beyond the scope of this book that the equilibrium value is that which causes the Fermi level to be continuous across the boundary. In terms of Fig. 5.2 this gives:

$$qV_B = \Delta E + \Delta E' \tag{5.1}$$

$V_B$ is dimensionally a voltage and is usually called the 'barrier voltage'.

The reader is reminded that in diagrams such as Fig. 5.2 the vertical axis is electron energy. This convention means that in Fig. 5.2(b), for instance, a conduction band electron will fall downhill from the p- to the n-side, as noted above. A hole in the valence band, on the other hand, will 'fall' up-hill, from the n- to the p-side, due to its positive charge. (This can be confirmed by looking at the signs of the charges in Fig. 5.1.) An inelegant, but remarkably useful, way of looking at this is to think of electrons in the conduction band as balls, and holes in the valence band as bubbles.

### 5.2.1  Calculation of $V_B$

The requirement that the Fermi level should be continuous at equilibrium allows us to calculate $V_B$. We have already seen in Chapter 4 that the concentration of electrons in a semiconductor is given by the expression

$$n = 2\left[\frac{2\pi m_n kT}{h^2}\right]^{\frac{3}{2}} \exp\left(\frac{E_F - E_c}{kT}\right) \tag{5.2}$$

where $E_F$ is the Fermi energy and $E_c$ is the bottom of the conduction band. Consider first an intrinsic semiconductor. In this case, $n = p = n_i$. If the 'intrinsic' Fermi level is at energy $F_i$, equation (5.2) becomes

$$n_i = 2\left[\frac{2\pi m_n kT}{h^2}\right]^{\frac{3}{2}} \exp\left(\frac{F_i - E_c}{kT}\right) \tag{5.3}$$

Now add donors, turning the semiconductor n-type, and raising the Fermi level to $E_F = F_i + \Delta E$, as in Fig. 5.2. If the electron concentration in the n-type specimen is called $n_n$, we have

$$n_n = 2\left[\frac{2\pi m_n kT}{h^2}\right]^{\frac{3}{2}} \exp\left(\frac{(F_i + \Delta E) - E_c}{kT}\right) \tag{5.4}$$

i.e.   $$n_n = n_i \exp\frac{\Delta E}{kT} \tag{5.5}$$

by comparison of equations (5.4) and (5.3).

A similar argument can be rehearsed for holes in a p-type specimen. If the Fermi level is at distance $\Delta E'$ below $F_i$, as in Fig. 5.2, the concentration of holes in the valence band is given by

$$p_p = n_i \exp\left(\frac{\Delta E'}{kT}\right) \tag{5.6}$$

We then join the two specimens together, forming the junction. To find $V_B$ we need an expression for $(\Delta E + \Delta E')$. This can be achieved as follows:

$$n_n p_p = n_i^2 \exp\left(\frac{\Delta E + \Delta E'}{kT}\right) = n_i^2 \exp\left(\frac{qV_B}{kT}\right) \tag{5.7}$$

where equation (5.1) has been used. Hence

$$V_B = \frac{kT}{q} \ln\left(\frac{n_n p_p}{n_i^2}\right) \tag{5.8}$$

It was noted in Chapter 4 that, provided the semiconductors are not too heavily doped, it is a good approximation to write:

$$n_n = N_D \text{ for an n-type semiconductor}$$

and $p_p = N_A$ for a p-type

where $N_D$ is the concentration of donors on the n-side and $N_A$ is the concentration of acceptors on the p-side. Equation (5.8) then becomes

$$V_B = \frac{kT}{q} \ln\left(\frac{N_A N_D}{n_i^2}\right) \tag{5.9}$$

For a given semiconductor, the barrier voltage therefore depends on the temperature and the doping on each side of the junction. Consider, for example, a junction in silicon with $N_A = 1 \times 10^{22}\,\text{m}^{-3}$ and $N_D = 4 \times 10^{21}\,\text{m}^{-3}$. For this material, $n_i$ at room temperature is $1.6 \times 10^{16}\,\text{m}^{-3}$. Using equation (5.9), we have $V_B = 0.67$ volts at 300 K.

### 5.2.2 Calculation of depletion width

We now consider the width of the depletion region in the junction of Figs 5.1 and 5.2. The region contains a space-charge due to the fact that donors on the n-side and acceptors on the p-side have lost their accompanying electrons and holes. This gives rise to an electric field which, in turn, causes a difference in potential energy, $qV_B$, between the two parts of the specimen. There is thus a potential difference, across the junction (the so-called 'built-in' potential), as shown in Fig. 5.3. The variation in potential shown in Fig. 5.3 is merely another way of representing the variation in electron potential energy shown in Fig. 5.2. The diagrams are 'mirror images' of each other because of the reason already discussed in Section 5.2, namely that potential is defined for positive charge, whereas the electron has a negative charge. Thus the fact that the p-side of the junction is at a lower potential than the n-side, as shown in Fig. 5.3, means that the electrons on the p-side have a greater potential energy, as indicated in Fig. 5.2(b).

We assume that the numbers of electrons and holes in the depletion region are negligible and that all of the donors and acceptors are ionised. The regions of space-charge can therefore be described thus:

$$\rho = -qN_A \quad 0 > x > X_1$$
$$\rho = +qN_D \quad X_2 > x > 0$$
$$\rho = 0 \quad \text{elsewhere}$$

where $\rho$ is the density of space-charge in the regions indicated. Note that $V_1$ and $X_1$ must turn out to have negative values because of the way the axes have been chosen in Fig. 5.3.

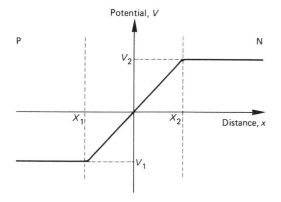

**Fig. 5.3** Variation in potential across a p–n junction

We first need to calculate the way in which the potential varies in the space-charge region. The standard way of doing this is to use Poisson's equation:

$$\nabla^2 V = -\frac{\rho(x, y, z)}{\epsilon_0 \epsilon_r}$$

where $\epsilon_r$ is relative permittivity. Here we have a one-dimensional problem, so the relevant equation is:

$$\frac{d^2 V}{dx^2} = -\frac{\rho}{\epsilon_0 \epsilon_r} \tag{5.10}$$

Apply equation (5.10) to the p-side of the junction:

$$\frac{d^2 V}{dx^2} = \frac{qN_A}{\epsilon_0 \epsilon_r}$$

Integrating twice gives

$$V = \frac{qN_A x^2}{2\epsilon_0 \epsilon_r} + Cx + D$$

where $C$ and $D$ are the constants of integration. In Fig. 5.3, we have $V = 0$ at $x = 0$, so $D = 0$. To find $C$, we make use of the fact that for $x < X_1$ on the p-side, the potential is constant, so that at $x = X_1$, $dV/dx = 0$. This gives:

$$C = -\frac{qN_A}{\epsilon_0 \epsilon_r} \cdot X_1$$

i.e.

$$V = \frac{qN_A}{\epsilon_0 \epsilon_r}\left(\frac{x^2}{2} - X_1 x\right) \tag{5.11}$$

Now, at $x = X_1$, $V = V_1$, i.e.

$$V_1 = -\frac{qN_A X_1^2}{2\epsilon_0 \epsilon_r} \tag{5.12}$$

Applying the same argument to the n-side, we have

$$V_2 = \frac{qN_D X_2^2}{2\epsilon_0 \epsilon_r} \tag{5.13}$$

Now the total built-in potential is $V_B$, where

$$V_B = V_2 - V_1 = \frac{q}{2\epsilon_0 \epsilon_r}(N_A X_1^2 + N_D X_2^2) \tag{5.14}$$

The final piece of information to be used is that the positive charge on the n-side must be equal in magnitude to the negative charge on the p-side, otherwise the specimen would not be neutral, i.e.

$$N_A X_1 = -N_D X_2 \tag{5.15}$$

(remember that $X_1$ is a negative quantity). Eliminating $X_2$ from equations (5.14) and (5.15) gives

$$X_1 = -\left[\frac{2\epsilon_0 \epsilon_r V_B}{qN_A\left(1 + \dfrac{N_A}{N_D}\right)}\right]^{\frac{1}{2}} \tag{5.16}$$

Similarly,

$$X_2 = \left[\frac{2\epsilon_0 \epsilon_r V_B}{qN_D\left(1 + \dfrac{N_D}{N_A}\right)}\right]^{\frac{1}{2}} \tag{5.17}$$

The total depletion width, $W = X_2 - X_1$, can now be found. The algebra required to do this is simple but rather tedious. The trick is to write $W$ in the form: $W^2 = X_1^2 + X_2^2 - 2X_1X_2$ and then substitute for $X_1$ and $X_2$ from equations (5.16) and (5.17). The result is:

$$W = \left[ \frac{2\epsilon_0\epsilon_r V_B}{q} \left( \frac{N_A + N_D}{N_A N_D} \right) \right]^{\frac{1}{2}} \tag{5.18}$$

## 5.3 The diode rectifier

Mention has been made above of the fact that the p–n junction has special properties which are useful in devices. Probably the most important is that of rectification. If electrical contacts are made to the p- and n-portions on each side of a junction, as in Fig. 5.4, then a current can be passed across the junction. It is found that current passes much more easily in one direction than in the other. In this section a simple argument will be given leading to the rectifier equation for a p–n junction.

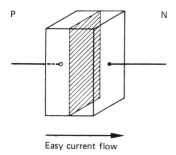

**Fig. 5.4** Junction rectifier

It is first necessary to enquire a little more closely into the mechanism whereby the energy barrier $qV_B$ manages to equalise the currents flowing at equilibrium across the junction. We have seen that there are four such currents; they are indicated by arrows in Fig. 5.5. A hole current $I_2$ flows in the valence band of the junction, and an electron current $-I_1$ flows in the conduction band. The negative sign for electron current is a consequence of the fact that a positive flow of electrons constitutes a negative current, i.e. the arrows indicate the directions of flow of electrons. The reader is reminded of the rule of thumb given for this sort of diagram; electrons in the conduction band roll down-hill, like balls, and holes in the valence band float up-hill, like bubbles.

Let us simplify matters for the moment by considering only electrons; the argument for holes is exactly analogous. The electrons in the conduction band can be thought of as small particles, flying about at random within the semiconductor, undergoing many collisions. Every so often an electron on the p-side will arrive at the edge of the depletion region, travelling in the general direction of the n-side. The electric field in the region will immediately grip hold of this electron and transport it to the n-side of the junction. This fate is in store for any electron that happens to find itself at the left-hand side of the depletion region. The flow of electrons thus produced gives rise to the current $-I_1$ left–right across the junction. The current $-I_1$ is insensitive to the height of the energy barrier; its magnitude is determined simply by the random arrival of electrons at the top of the hill. Similar random processes will bring electrons on the n-side to the edge of the depletion region. They cannot all cross the junction, however; only those with sufficient energy to climb the energy barrier can cross. Thus although there are many electrons on the n-side, only a small percentage is eligible to cross the junction and contribute to the current $-I_1$ flowing right to left.

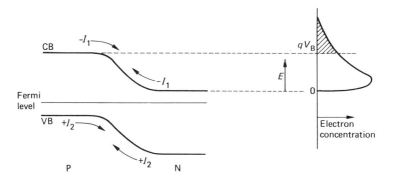

**Fig. 5.5**  Energy band diagram at zero bias showing number of conduction band electrons able to cross N→P

It is worth looking closely into how many electrons on the n-side could possibly cross to the p-side. The distribution of electrons in the conduction band was described in Chapter 4 and given as a function of energy in the form

$$n(E) = F(E)S_c(E) \qquad (5.19)$$

where $F(E)$ is the Fermi function, given by equation (4.13), and $S_c(E)$ is the density of states function, given by equation (4.10). If the simplified form of the Fermi function, equation (4.16), is used and the bottom of the conduction band, $E_c$, is taken as the zero of energy, then equation (5.19) simplifies to

$$n(E) = KE^{\frac{1}{2}}\exp\left(-\frac{E}{kT}\right) \qquad (5.20)$$

where $K$ is a constant which includes effective mass, Fermi energy, etc. Inspection of equation (5.20) shows that, starting from the bottom of the conduction band, the function increases from zero as $E^{\frac{1}{2}}$, but that the decreasing exponential term soon dominates, and thereafter the concentration of electrons decreases very sharply with increasing energy.

Equation (5.20) has been plotted on Fig. 5.5. It is clear that only those electrons in the tail of the distribution on the n-side have energy greater than $qV_B$, and are eligible to cross the junction. The number that can do so is given by the area under the curve, shown shaded in Fig. 5.5. This area can be expressed thus:

$$K' \int_{qV_B}^{\infty} \exp\left(-\frac{E}{kT}\right) dE = K'kT\exp\left(-\frac{qV_B}{kT}\right) \tag{5.21}$$

Now apply a forward voltage, $V$, to the junction, i.e. apply a battery to make the p-side positive with respect to the n-side. We assume that all of this voltage is dropped at the junction. This is reasonable since the junction, being a region depleted of carriers, has a very high electrical resistance. Since Fig.

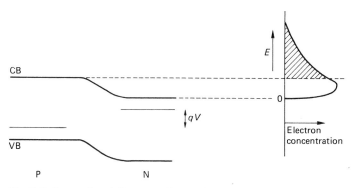

**Fig. 5.6** Energy band diagram at forward bias, showing increased number of conduction band electrons able to cross N → P

5.5 is an electron energy diagram, the effect of the voltage is to bring about a reduction in potential energy on the p-side of the junction. The entire left-hand side moves down relative to the right-hand side by an amount $qV$, so that the height of the barrier at the junction is reduced by that amount. The situation is shown in Fig. 5.6. The Fermi level no longer lines up across the junction; the difference in levels is $qV$. It can be seen from the figure that the reduction in barrier height from $qV_B$ to $q(V_B - V)$ has a dramatic effect on the number of electrons eligible to cross from the n-side to the p-side of the junction. The new number is:

$$K' \int_{q(V_B - V)}^{\infty} \exp\left(-\frac{E}{kT}\right) dE = K'kT\exp\left(-\frac{q(V_B - V)}{kT}\right) \tag{5.22}$$

Comparison of equations (5.21) and (5.22) shows that the application of the voltage has increased the number of electrons that can cross from n to p by a factor $\exp(qV/kT)$.

We are now in a position to derive the $I$–$V$ characteristic of the junction. Consider the changes in the four currents which flow across the junction upon the application of the forward bias, $V$:

(i) Electrons left–right. Nothing changes. The flow of electrons down the hill is fixed by the number of electrons arriving by random motion at the top. The current therefore stays at $-I_1$.

(ii) Electrons right–left. The barrier that must be crossed is now reduced by an amount $qV$. According to the argument given above, the number of electrons eligible to cross the barrier increases by a factor $\exp(qV/kT)$. The current must therefore increase by the same factor to $-I_1 \exp(qV/kT)$.

(iii) Holes left–right. The barrier that must be climbed by the holes is reduced by $qV$. The current therefore increases from $I_2$ to $I_2 \exp(qV/kT)$.

(iv) Holes right–left. The current stays at $I_2$, for the same reason as that given in (i), above.

The total current across the junction is the sum of the four outlined in (i) to (iv), taking due account of the signs involved. Some care is needed here because of the negative signs on the electron arrows in Fig. 5.5. We will define the positive direction of current flow as p→n; it is given by

$$I = (I_1 + I_2)\left( \exp\left(\frac{qV}{kT}\right) - 1 \right) \tag{5.23}$$

Generally speaking, it is convenient to work in terms of current density, $J$, rather than current, $I$. The diode equation is thus usually expressed

$$J = J_0\left( \exp\left(\frac{qV}{kT}\right) - 1 \right) \tag{5.24}$$

where $J_0 = (I_1 + I_2)/A$ and $A$ is the area of the junction. The $J$–$V$ characteristic is plotted in Fig. 5.7. It will be remembered that the definition given for $V$ makes it positive when the p-side of the junction is positive with respect to the n-side. The rectifying property of the junction is clear. For positive $V$ the current increases sharply, approximately exponentially. For negative $V$ the barrier at the junction becomes larger instead of smaller. The currents (ii) and (iii) decrease exponentially and the diode current saturates at $-J_0$ which might typically be of the order of $10^{-6}$ A m$^{-2}$ in a silicon device.

If a sufficiently large reverse bias is applied to the junction then a sharp increase in reverse current can be obtained. This phenomenon is called breakdown and is illustrated in Fig. 5.7.

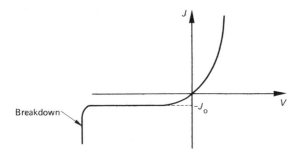

**Fig. 5.7**

## 5.4 Fractions of diode current carried by electrons and holes

When a forward current is passed through a p–n junction it is carried partly by electrons and partly by holes. The relative magnitudes of these two components are determined by the relative doping of the n- and p-sides of the junction. This can be seen by the following argument.

Consider the p–n junction of Fig. 5.5 and assume, for the sake of argument, that the values of $I_1$ and $I_2$ are initially about the same. Now imagine that we can suddenly increase the doping on the n-side. This increase must raise the concentration of electrons in the conduction band on the n-side, $n_n$, and lower the concentration of holes, $p_n$. The concentrations of electrons and holes on the p-side, $n_p$ and $p_p$, are unaffected. The other important effect of increasing the doping on the n-side is to bring the Fermi level closer to the conduction band on that side. Inspection of the figure shows that this results in increasing the height of the barrier at the junction, $qV_B$. We can now consider how these changes affect the values of the four currents, using much the same reasoning as in Section 5.3.

 (i) Electrons left–right. The flow of electrons down the hill is determined by $n_p$, which has not changed. The fact that the hill is higher makes no difference. Current therefore stays at $-I_1$.
 (ii) Electrons right–left. The number of electrons available to climb the hill is increased, since $n_n$ has increased, and it might be thought that more electrons will climb the hill. This is not the case, however, since the hill is now higher. At equilibrium the same number as before climb the hill and the current remains at $-I_1$.
 (iii) Holes left–right. The number of holes on the p-side available to 'climb' p to n is the same as before, $p_p$, but the height of the hill is now greater. Current therefore decreases to $I_2'$.
 (iv) Holes right–left. The number of holes arriving by random motion at the top of the energy hill is now decreased, because $p_n$ has decreased. Current decreases to a value $I_2'$ at equilibrium.

Thus the effect of increasing $N_D$ on the n-side is to make no difference to the electron current across the junction, but to decrease the hole current. When a voltage $V$ is applied, equation (5.23) becomes

$$ I = (I_1 + I_2') \left( \exp\left(\frac{qV}{kT}\right) - 1 \right) \tag{5.25} $$

where $I_2' < I_2$

For a given current flowing across the junction, this means that the greater part is carried by electrons. Similarly if the p-side of a junction is doped much more heavily than the n-side, most of the current is carried by holes. This effect is important in the bipolar transistor, which must be designed in such a way as to make most of the current crossing the emitter junction to be due to carriers passing emitter–base rather than base–emitter.

## 5.5 Depletion region capacitance

At the p–n junction are two space-charge regions, facing each other and containing equal and opposite amounts of charge, $|Q|$, per unit area of junction. From equation (5.15)

$$|Q| = -qN_A X_1 = qN_D X_2$$

where $X_1$ and $X_2$ are given by equations (5.16) and (5.17) respectively. If a forward bias $V$ is applied to the junction, then the term $V_B$ in equations (5.16) and (5.17) becomes $(V_B - V)$ and we have

$$|Q| = -qN_A X_1 = \left[ \frac{2q\epsilon_0 \epsilon_r N_A N_D}{N_A + N_D} \right]^{\frac{1}{2}} (V_B - V)^{\frac{1}{2}} \qquad (5.26)$$

The amount of charge therefore changes as the applied voltage changes, i.e. there is an incremental capacitance $C$ which is given by

$$C = A \frac{dQ}{d(V_B - V)} = A \left[ \frac{q\epsilon_0 \epsilon_r N_A N_D}{2(N_A + N_D)} \right]^{\frac{1}{2}} (V_B - V)^{-\frac{1}{2}} \qquad (5.27)$$

where $A$ is the junction area. (Note that if the diode is reverse-biased, $V$ becomes a negative quantity.) The capacitance is thus voltage-dependent. This calculation is correct for an abrupt junction; if some other type of junction had been chosen a slightly different result would have been obtained. Comparison with equation (5.18) shows that the capacitance can alternatively be written

$$C = \frac{\epsilon_0 \epsilon_r A}{W} \qquad (5.28)$$

i.e. it has the same form as that for a parallel-plate capacitor with the depletion width $W$ replacing the distance between the plates. A typical value of $C$ for a silicon diode of area 1 mm$^2$ might be of the order of 100 pF.

The existence of depletion-region capacitance means that p–n junctions can be used in circuits as variable capacitors. They are useful in this respect only under conditions of reverse-bias. When the device is forward biased it still has capacitance, but it also passes a substantial current and this makes it a rather unsatisfactory 'leaky' capacitor. Under conditions of forward bias a second source of capacitance also becomes significant. This is called diffusion capacitance and is due to the charges built up by electrons injected into the p-side and holes injected into the n-side. Diffusion capacitance is important in transistor operation because it determines the rate at which the device can be turned on and off.

## 5.6 Problems

Problems marked * are considered in the computer package (see Preface).

**5.1**    A p–n junction is made in a bar of silicon of cross-sectional area 1 mm$^2$ and length 3 mm. The junction is half-way along the bar and perpendicular to the length. The free electron concentration is $8.4 \times 10^{20}$ m$^{-3}$ on one side of the junction and $1.3 \times 10^{11}$ m$^{-3}$ on the other. Calculate the barrier height of the junction.

When a reverse voltage of 1 V is applied, a current of 1 $\mu$A flows. Calculate the voltage dropped across the device when a forward current of 10 mA is passing through it.

**5.2**    Find the magnitude of the barrier in an abrupt silicon junction in which the p-side is doped with one boron atom for each $10^6$ silicon atoms, and in which the n-side is doped with one phosphorus atom for each $5 \times 10^7$ silicon atoms.

Take the temperature to be 300 K, the density of silicon to be 2400 kg m$^{-3}$, its relative atomic mass to be 28.1 and the intrinsic charge carrier density to be $1.5 \times 10^{16}$ m$^{-3}$.

**5.3***    (i) A crystal of pure germanium has sufficient antimony added to produce $1.5 \times 10^{22}$ antimony atoms m$^{-3}$. The electron and hole mobilities are 0.38 m$^2$ V$^{-1}$ s$^{-1}$ and 0.18 m$^2$ V$^{-1}$ s$^{-1}$ respectively, and the intrinsic charge carrier density is $2.5 \times 10^{19}$ m$^{-3}$. Calculate
  (a) the density of electrons and holes in the crystal, and
  (b) the conductivity.
(ii) A second germanium crystal is produced which is doped with $2.5 \times 10^{22}$ indium atoms m$^{-3}$. Repeat the calculations listed in part (i).
(iii) A p–n junction is made by joining the two crystals described above. Calculate its barrier voltage at 300 K.

**5.4**    When a p–n junction is used in practice, it is usually the differential resistance, $dV/dI$, which is of interest rather than the resistance, $V/I$.

Why is this? Show that the differential resistance for a forward-biased junction is approximately given by:

$$r \simeq \frac{kT}{qI}$$

**5.5***    The current in a p–n junction diode is related to the voltage across it by the equation

$$I = 10^{-6}(e^{39V} - 1)$$

One side of the diode is connected to ground and the other through a resistor of 10 k$\Omega$ to a 10 V supply, such that the diode is forward-biased.

Obtain an approximate value for the current by graphical means.

If you are familiar with numerical techniques, you might like to try solving the problem as follows. Formulate a fixed point numerical solution for the voltage $V$ at the junction of the diode and the resistor in the form

$$V_{k+1} = f(V_k)$$

where $V_k$ is the voltage $V$ calculated at the $k$th numerical iteration. Work out a few iterations and show that the scheme does not readily converge.

Reformulate the problem in terms of the current through the circuit in the form

$$I_{k+1} = f(I_k)$$

and calculate the current to an accuracy of $0.01 \ \mu A$.

# 6 The Bipolar Transistor

The bipolar transistor is one of the most important of the semiconductor devices available to the electronics engineer. Probably its most common use is in amplifier circuits but it is also able to perform many other functions in analogue electronics. In addition it can operate as a fast switch and in this capacity forms the basis of a number of families of digital logic. In the present chapter we consider the physical form of the transistor and the way that current passes through it. We then show how it operates as an amplifier when in the common-emitter configuration.

The transistor consists of two back-to-back p–n junctions made in the same piece of semiconducting material. The two possible configurations, namely p–n–p and n–p–n, are shown in Fig. 6.1, together with the appropriate circuit symbols. The device has three terminals, called emitter, base and collector. Note that the emitter is identified on the circuit symbol by an arrow and that the direction, p→n, identifies the transistor type. In normal conditions in analogue circuits the device is operated with the emitter–base junction under forward bias and the collector–base junction under reverse bias. One way of arranging this is shown in Fig. 6.2 and it will be seen that in both cases $|V_{CE}|$ must be greater than $|V_{BE}|$ to obtain the required bias condition. The sign convention for indicating voltages should also be noted at this point. If a voltage is applied between A and B, then $V_{AB}$ represents the potential of A with respect to B. In Fig. 6.2 the positive and negative signs refer to the polarities of the supplies used to obtain the current bias. Thus $V_{CE}$ and $V_{BE}$ are negative quantities for the p–n–p device and positive for n–p–n.

The band diagram for the n–p–n structure is shown in Fig. 6.3. With no applied bias the Fermi level is continuous from collector to emitter (Fig. 6.3a)

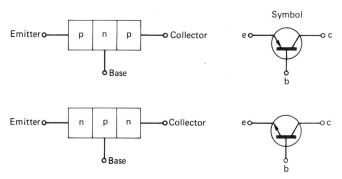

**Fig. 6.1** pnp and npn configurations

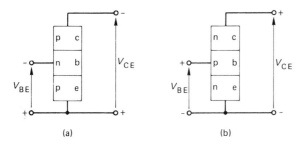

**Fig. 6.2**

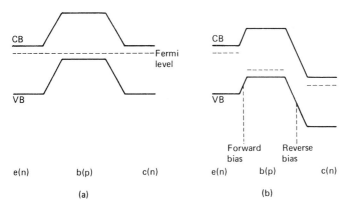

**Fig. 6.3** Energy band diagram for npn transistor with (a) zero-bias, (b) bias voltages applied as in Fig. 6.2(b)

and the two barrier heights are approximately equal. With bias applied as in Fig. 6.2, the Fermi levels in the three layers are at different energies and the emitter–base barrier height is less than that for the collector–base junction (Fig. 6.3b). A forward current flows p→n across the emitter junction, dominated by two components.

(i) Holes passing base–emitter. These cross the emitter and leave by the emitter contact, and play no part in the transistor action.
(ii) Electrons injected emitter–base. They diffuse across the base and those that reach the far side are swept into the collector by the base–collector junction field.

Since only the second component is useful from the point of view of transistor action, it is obviously desirable that the electron current should exceed that due to holes. Reference to Section 5.4 shows that this can be arranged by doping the emitter much more heavily than the base. This is what is usually done (it is not difficult to make a difference of at least two orders of magnitude) and we will assume that virtually all emitter current in the n–p–n transistor is carried by electrons. Not all electrons which are injected into the base reach the collector junction, however, since recombinations with majority holes can take place. The lost majority holes are replaced by way of the base contact, giving rise to base current. In order to reduce these

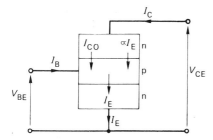

**Fig. 6.4** Current flow through the transistor

recombinations to a minimum, the width of the base is made as small as possible. Suppose a fraction $\alpha$ of the electron current reaches the far side of the base and enters the collector; the currents flowing into and through the device are then as in Fig. 6.4. Note that the flow of electrons into the base appears on the diagram as a flow of current from base to emitter and that the normal reverse-bias saturation current, $I_{CO}$, must flow across the collector junction.

Since all current which crosses the collector junction must initially flow in by the collector contact, we can write

$$I_C = \alpha I_E + I_{CO} \tag{6.1}$$

where $\alpha$ is likely to be at least 0.99. Treating the transistor as a node into which there can be no net flow of current,

$$I_E = I_B + I_C \tag{6.2}$$

## 6.1  Transistor as a circuit element

Any active circuit element requires four terminals: two for input voltages and currents and two for the output. The bipolar transistor has only three terminals so it follows that one of these must be common to both the input and

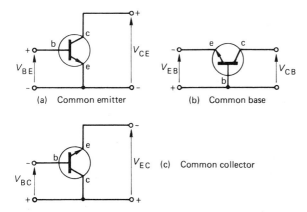

**Fig. 6.5** Three modes of operation for bipolar transistor

output sides. This gives the three possible modes of operation illustrated for an n–p–n transistor in Fig. 6.5: common emitter, common base and common collector. In each of these diagrams the input side is on the left and the output side is on the right. Of the three, the common emitter configuration is the most important and will be the only one considered in any detail in this book.

## 6.2 Input and output characteristics in the common emitter configuration

Figure 6.5(a) indicates that in the common emitter configuration the input characteristic is the graph of $I_B$ against $V_{BE}$. Its form is shown in Fig. 6.6. It looks very much like an $I$–$V$ curve for a p–n junction under forward bias, as might be expected, although it is not simply the forward characteristic of the

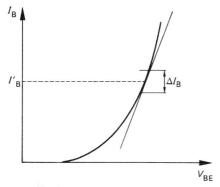

**Fig. 6.6**  Input characteristic in common-emitter mode

emitter junction since $I_B$ represents only a small fraction of the total emitter current. Figure 6.6 is drawn for a constant value of collector voltage, $V_{CE}$, because it is found that the curve is slightly sensitive to variations in this voltage. The reason for this is interesting. It was shown in Chapter 5 that the depletion width of a p–n junction depends on the applied voltage and that for a reverse-biased junction, the width increases if the bias is increased (equation 5.26)). If $V_{CE}$ is made larger, the depletion region of the base–collector junction encroaches further into the base and effectively makes it thinner. Since the minority electrons now have a shorter distance to travel across the base, fewer recombinations take place, so the base current is reduced. Increasing $V_{CE}$ therefore causes a small reduction in $I_B$ on Fig. 6.6.

When used as an amplifier the transistor is operated with a steady value of base current, $I'_B$ say, on which is superimposed the small a.c. signal which is to be amplified, $\Delta I_B$. The input resistance of the device to a.c. is therefore the slope of the input characteristic, $dV_{BE}/dI_B$ at $I'_B$. This can be calculated as follows.

Eliminating $I_c$ from equations (6.1) and (6.2) gives

$$I_B = I_E(1 - \alpha) - I_{CO} \tag{6.3}$$

so input resistance $r$ is given by

$$\frac{1}{r} = \frac{dI_B}{dV_{BE}} = (1 - \alpha)\frac{dI_E}{dV_{BE}} \tag{6.4}$$

The total emitter current is

$$I_E = I_{EO}\left(\exp\left(\frac{qV_{BE}}{kT}\right) - 1\right) \tag{6.5}$$

where $I_{EO}$ is the reverse bias saturation current for the emitter junction.

$$\frac{dI_E}{dV_{BE}} = \frac{qI_{EO}}{kT}\exp\left(\frac{qV_{BE}}{kT}\right) \simeq \frac{qI_E}{kT} \tag{6.6}$$

so, from equation (6.4),

$$\frac{1}{r} \simeq \frac{q}{kT}(1 - \alpha)I_E \tag{6.7}$$

If we assume that $I_{CO}$ in equation (6.3) is negligible, as would normally be the case, equations (6.3) and (6.7) combine to give

$$r \simeq \frac{kT}{qI_B} \tag{6.8}$$

It follows that the input resistance depends on the value chosen for $I'_B$. If a base current of 0.1 mA is used, for instance, $r$ is 260 $\Omega$ at room temperature. An ohmic component should also be added, due to the resistance of the base.

The output characteristic is obtained by plotting $V_{CE}$ against $I_C$. This is not a single curve, since $I_C$ depends on the magnitude of the current crossing the emitter junction which, in turn, depends on the forward voltage on the emitter. The characteristic is therefore a family of curves. Conventionally, each $V_{CE}$ v. $I_C$ curve is plotted for a single value of $I_B$, as shown in Fig. 6.7. A curve has two main parts: a steeply rising portion for low collector voltage and an almost horizontal portion for higher voltages. Consider the one for $I_B = 4a$, with reference to Fig. 6.4. At the origin, with $V_{CE} = 0$, the emitter and collector are at the same potential. Since $V_{BE} > 0$, both emitter and collector junctions are forward biased. As $V_{CE}$ is increased, the forward bias on the collector junction diminishes. The collector field is in the right direction to collect electrons from the emitter side of the base, but the collector junction is itself injecting electrons into the base because of its own forward bias. The 'knee' in the curve of Fig. 6.7 corresponds to the value of $V_{CE}$ at which the collector junction loses its forward bias. Any further increase in $V_{CE}$ causes the collector junction to go into reverse bias, and the normal operating region of the device is entered. Once the collector junction has a reverse bias it simply collects all electrons which diffuse across from the

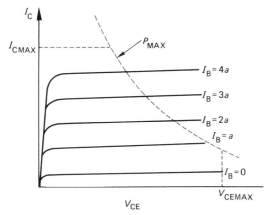

**Fig. 6.7** Output characteristic in common-emitter mode

emitter side of the base and $I_C$ increases only slowly with increasing $V_{CE}$. The output resistance of the device is given by the slope of the 'horizontal' portion.

At first sight it would appear that the curves should be accurately horizontal for $V_{CE}$ above the knee, since once the collector is gathering 100% of the electrons diffusing across the base, there is no obvious reason why $I_C$ should increase any further. The explanation is to be found in the base width narrowing which has already been described. As $V_{CE}$ is increased, the base narrows and more of the injected electrons reach the collector junction. This has the effect of reducing $I_B$, which is not permitted, because the curves of Fig. 6.7 are all plotted for constant $I_B$. In order to keep $I_B$ at $4a$, say, it is therefore necessary to increase $V_{BE}$ slightly. This also increases $I_C$, so the observed rise is obtained.

For a given transistor, the manufacturer will usually indicate the range in which it can be safely operated. Thus a maximum collector current $I_{CMAX}$, collector voltage $V_{CEMAX}$ and maximum power $(I_C V_{CE})_{MAX}$ are given. These are indicated on Fig. 6.7; the device can be used within the region to the left of the dotted lines. Operation beyond these limits will cause over-heating of the device, or breakdown of the collector junction (see Fig. 5.7).

## 6.3 Amplification in the common emitter mode

A simple amplifying circuit is shown in Fig. 6.8. The transistor is connected in series with a d.c. supply, $V_{cc}$ and a collector resistor, $R_C$. A steady current $I_B$ enters the base. Note that if a p–n–p transistor had been chosen, the supply voltage would have been negative and the currents would have been in the opposite directions. The signal to be amplified is applied between base and emitter, adding a small alternating current to the base, $i_B$, say. The voltages across the transistor and the collector resistor must add up to the supply voltage, so we can write

$$V_{cc} = V_{CE} + I_C R_C \tag{6.9}$$

where all symbols represent positive quantities.

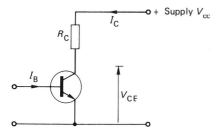

**Fig. 6.8** Amplification in the common-emitter mode

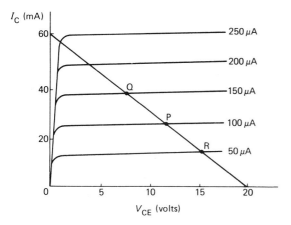

**Fig. 6.9** Load line plotted on set of output characteristics

A typical set of characteristics is shown in Fig. 6.9. They are slightly idealised inasmuch as the curves are parallel and equally spaced. We will consider deviations from this ideal condition a little later. Note that it follows from equations (6.1) and (6.2) that if $\alpha$ is close to unity the values of $I_B$ on the diagram must be small compared to the values of $I_C$. Suppose we choose a quiescent base current of 100 $\mu$A, a supply of 20 volts and a collector resistor of 333 $\Omega$. The choice of base current constrains the transistor to operate on the 100 $\mu$A curve. A further constraint on the circuit is given by equation (6.9) which in this case becomes

$$20 = V_{CE} + 333 I_C \qquad (6.10)$$

and can be plotted as a straight line, known as the load line, on the same graph. The point at which the load line intersects the 100 $\mu$A curve gives the working point of the circuit, P. This point represents the state of the circuit when no a.c. signal is being applied to the base.

Now present to the base an a.c. signal varying between +50 $\mu$A and $-50$ $\mu$A. The system then moves between points Q and R on the figure with a frequency given by the frequency of the signal. The two points correspond to a difference in output current $I_C$ of about 20 mA. Thus an input signal of 100 $\mu$A peak-to-peak has given rise to an output signal of 20 mA, i.e. a current amplification of about 200 has been achieved.

Much the same result can be obtained by a consideration of equations (6.1) and (6.2). If emitter current $I_E$ is eliminated from the two equations, the following is obtained

$$I_C = \left(\frac{\alpha}{1-\alpha}\right) I_B + \frac{I_{CO}}{1-\alpha} \qquad (6.11)$$

Putting $\left(\dfrac{\alpha}{1-\alpha}\right) = \beta$, we obtain

$$I_C = \beta I_B + (\beta + 1) I_{CO} \qquad (6.12)$$

where $\beta$ is called the current amplification factor. A typical value for $\alpha$ might be 0.995 giving about 200 for $\beta$. Thus equation (6.12) indicates that small variations in $I_B$ give rise to variations in $I_C$ some 200 times greater. (Remember that the second term on the right-hand side of equation (6.12) is simply a very small constant.)

## 6.4  Selection of working point

The working point P must clearly be chosen in such a way that the transistor is always operating within the permitted area indicated in Fig. 6.7. In addition it should be within a region of the characteristics where the curves are as evenly spaced as possible. The collector resistance is chosen so that when the a.c. signal is applied the operating point moves within a region where the curves are approximately horizontal. If the point strays onto the vertical portion, severe distortion can result.

Having chosen the point P it is necessary to ensure that the required base current $I_B$ is flowing. This is arranged by connecting the base to the supply through a resistor $R_1$, as in Fig. 6.10. The voltage across the resistor is $(V_{cc} - V_{BE})$ so the resistance required is given by

$$R_1 = \frac{V_{cc} - V_{BE}}{I_B} \qquad (6.13)$$

$V_{BE}$ is the voltage drop across the forward-biased emitter junction and is typically a fraction of a volt. This will often be very small compared to $V_{cc}$ and, to a good approximation,

$$R_1 \simeq \frac{V_{cc}}{I_B} \qquad (6.14)$$

Thus in the example of Section 6.3, a bias resistor of about 20 V/100 $\mu$A $\simeq$ 200 k$\Omega$ would be required. This method represents the simplest way of achieving the required base current; more sophisticated techniques exist which can give better stability. For these the reader is referred to books on transistor circuitry.

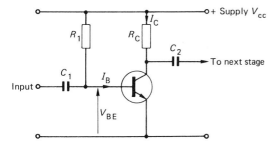

**Fig. 6.10** Common-emitter amplifier stage

Generally speaking, a given amplifier stage will be just one in a sequence of stages, i.e. it will be accepting a signal from a previous one and handing it on to the next. It is desirable that the setting up of the d.c. conditions, as outlined above, should be carried out individually for each stage. This presents a problem since the output from a given stage will normally contain a d.c. component superimposed on the a.c. signal. The d.c. is removed by the use of the decoupling capacitors $C_1$, $C_2$ in Fig. 6.10. These prevent the passing on of d.c. between stages. The values chosen for $C_1$ and $C_2$ are such as to give the capacitors very low impedance at the frequency of the a.c. signal.

## 6.5 Distortion

It has already been mentioned that the set of characteristics given in Fig. 6.9 is somewhat idealised; the 'horizontal' portions of the curves are accurately parallel and equally spaced. This will not be the case for a real transistor, so the change in $I_C$ in going from P to Q, for instance, will not be exactly the same as the change in going from P to R. This introduces distortion into the output signal, which will not be excessive providing the swing about P is not too large. The region in which the distortion can be considered negligible is called the small-signal region of operation. Within this region, transistor parameters such as current amplification factor, $\beta$, can be defined and used to analyse circuit performance (as in equation (6.12), for example). If small-signal operation cannot be assumed, however, the transistor parameters can no longer be considered as simple constants and it is necessary to go back to the transistor characteristics to predict the behaviour of a circuit, as described in Section 6.3.

## 6.6 Small-signal equivalent circuit

Within the region of small-signal operation, it is possible to describe the bipolar transistor by a simple equivalent circuit. A number of such circuits exist; in this section we describe one of the most useful, the $h$-parameter network.

Consider any amplifier inside a 'black box'. The box must have two input terminals and two output terminals to which currents and voltages can be assigned, as in Fig. 6.11. By convention the currents are drawn as entering the

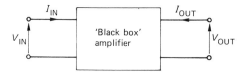

**Fig. 6.11**

box at the upper terminals. For a given amplifier any two of the set $I_{\text{IN}}$, $I_{\text{OUT}}$, $V_{\text{IN}}$, $V_{\text{OUT}}$ determine the other two. Let us specify $V_{\text{IN}}$ and $I_{\text{OUT}}$ in terms of $I_{\text{IN}}$, $V_{\text{OUT}}$, i.e.

$$V_{\text{IN}} = f(I_{\text{IN}}, V_{\text{OUT}}) \qquad (6.15a)$$

$$I_{\text{OUT}} = f(I_{\text{IN}}, V_{\text{OUT}}) \qquad (6.15b)$$

We are not usually interested in the absolute values of these quantities but in small changes in them (i.e. the a.c. signal). Hence equations (6.15a) and (6.15b) can be written in the differential form

$$\delta V_{\text{IN}} = \left(\frac{\partial V_{\text{IN}}}{\partial I_{\text{IN}}}\right)_{V_{\text{OUT}}} \delta I_{\text{IN}} + \left(\frac{\partial V_{\text{IN}}}{\partial V_{\text{OUT}}}\right)_{I_{\text{IN}}} \delta V_{\text{OUT}} \qquad (6.16a)$$

$$\delta I_{\text{OUT}} = \left(\frac{\partial I_{\text{OUT}}}{\partial I_{\text{IN}}}\right)_{V_{\text{OUT}}} \delta I_{\text{IN}} + \left(\frac{\partial I_{\text{OUT}}}{\partial V_{\text{OUT}}}\right)_{I_{\text{IN}}} \delta V_{\text{OUT}} \qquad (6.16b)$$

The notation can be simplified by using small letters to indicate incremental values and symbols to represent the differentials. Equations (6.16a) and (6.16b) become

$$v_{\text{in}} = h_i i_{\text{in}} + h_r v_{\text{out}} \qquad (6.17a)$$

$$i_{\text{out}} = h_f i_{\text{in}} + h_0 v_{\text{out}} \qquad (6.17b)$$

The reason for the choice of subscripts on the $h$-parameters will become clear later.

Suppose the black box contains a bipolar transistor working in the common emitter mode. Then equations (6.15a) and (6.15b) become

$$V_{\text{BE}} = f(I_{\text{B}}, V_{\text{CE}}) \qquad (6.18a)$$

$$I_{\text{C}} = f(I_{\text{B}}, V_{\text{CE}}) \qquad (6.18b)$$

which, by analogy with equations (6.17a) and (6.17b), lead to

$$v_{\text{be}} = h_{\text{ie}} i_{\text{b}} + h_{\text{re}} v_{\text{ce}} \qquad (6.19a)$$

$$i_{\text{c}} = h_{\text{fe}} i_{\text{b}} + h_{\text{oe}} v_{\text{ce}} \qquad (6.19b)$$

where the extra 'e' subscript is added to the parameters to indicate 'common-emitter mode'. Similarly for a transistor connected in the common base configuration, four different parameters $h_{ib}$, $h_{rb}$, $h_{fb}$, $h_{ob}$ would be defined. Any circuit which obeys equations (6.19a) and (6.19b) constitutes an acceptable model for the bipolar transistor under conditions of small-signal operation. Such a circuit is given in Fig. 6.12, in which the input side is modelled by a voltage source in series with a resistance and the output side is a current source in parallel with a resistance. Note that the circuit includes only the a.c. components of the voltages and currents.

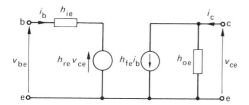

**Fig. 6.12** Small-signal equivalent circuit using $h$-parameters

The physical significance of the $h$-parameters for the common-emitter mode can be understood as follows; referring to equations (6.19a), (6.19b) and Fig. 6.12:

(i) $h_{ie} = v_{in}/i_{in}$ with $v_{out} = 0$ (i.e. with $V_{OUT} = $ constant).
This is the incremental input impedance or, to put it another way, the impedance seen by the a.c. signal, with the output short-circuited to a.c. The impedance has two main components, namely the incremental resistance of the emitter junction, given by equation (6.8), and the ohmic resistance of the base.

(ii) $h_{fe} = i_{out}/i_{in}$ with $v_{out} = 0$.
The incremental current gain with the output short-circuited to a.c. It corresponds to the quantity previously called $\beta$ in Section 6.3.

(iii) $h_{re} = v_{in}/v_{out}$ with $i_{in} = 0$.
The incremental reverse voltage ratio, a feedback term showing the way that the output voltage affects the voltage on the input side. This is the effect already discussed in Section 6.2 where it was shown that the output voltage $V_{CE}$ has a small effect on the input characteristics due to base-width narrowing at the collector junction. The effect is usually small and $h_{re}$ can often be neglected.

(iv) $h_{oe} = i_{out}/v_{out}$ with $i_{in} = 0$.
The incremental output admittance with input open-circuited to a.c., corresponding to the slope of the 'horizontal' portion of the output

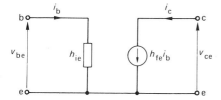

**Fig. 6.13** Simplified form of Fig. 6.12

characteristic. For most transistors this turns out to be a very low admittance and it can often be ignored in practical calculations.

When both $h_{re}$ and $h_{oe}$ can be neglected, a simplified form of equivalent circuit, shown in Fig. 6.13, is obtained.

## 6.7 Calculation of amplifier performance

Figure 6.14 shows a single stage amplifier in which an input voltage signal, $v_1$, is applied to the transistor base and the output $v_2$ is developed across a load, $R_4$. The problem is to calculate the voltage amplification $v_2/v_1$. In order to analyse the circuit we replace the transistor (shown enclosed by dotted lines) with its small-signal equivalent circuit. The reader is reminded that the equivalent circuit is concerned only with the a.c. signal and not the d.c.

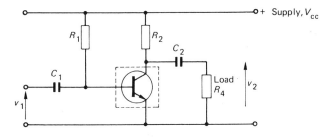

**Fig. 6.14**

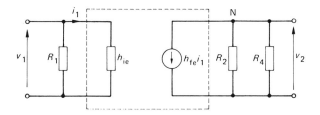

**Fig. 6.15** Equivalent circuit for Fig. 6.14 using simplified form for transistor

voltages which are there purely to give the correct operating conditions. The supply battery is considered to be a short-circuit to a.c. so the top and bottom lines on Fig. 6.14 are joined together for the a.c. components. This means, for instance, that $R_2$ and $R_4$ are in parallel as far as a.c. is concerned. The equivalent circuit, using the simplified form of Fig. 6.13, is shown in Fig. 6.15. It is assumed that the a.c. impedances of $C_1$ and $C_2$ are negligible. Applying Ohm's law to the input side, we have

$$i_1 = \frac{v_1}{h_{ie}}$$ (6.20)

At the node N,

$$h_{\mathrm{fe}}i_1 + \frac{v_2}{R_2} + \frac{v_2}{R_4} = 0 \tag{6.21}$$

Eliminating $i$ between these two equations gives

$$\frac{v_2}{v_1} = -\frac{h_{\mathrm{fe}}}{h_{\mathrm{ie}}}\left(\frac{R_2 R_4}{R_2 + R_4}\right) \tag{6.22}$$

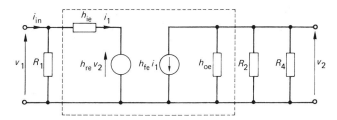

**Fig. 6.16** Equivalent circuit for Fig. 6.14 using full transistor circuit

If $C_1$ and $C_2$ are not omitted from the equivalent circuit the expressions become slightly more complicated (and dependent upon frequency) but the problem is basically no more difficult. If the full equivalent circuit of Fig. 6.12 is used, the circuit to be solved is the one shown in Fig. 6.16. Applying Kirchoff's law to the input mesh,

$$v_1 - h_{\mathrm{re}}v_2 = i_1 h_{\mathrm{ie}} \tag{6.23}$$

At the node N,

$$\frac{v_2}{R_4} + \frac{v_2}{R_2} + v_2 h_{\mathrm{oe}} + h_{\mathrm{fe}}i_1 = 0 \tag{6.24}$$

The voltage amplification $v_2/v_1$ is again found by eliminating $i_1$ from the equations. Note that $i_1$ is not the same as the input current to the circuit, $i_{\mathrm{in}}$, since some current flows through the bias resistor, $R_1$. However, if $R_1$ is much greater than the input resistance of the transistor, as is usually the case, the distinction can often be ignored.

## 6.8 High frequency operation

It was shown in Chapter 5 that any p–n junction has capacitance. Thus in addition to the capacitors $C_1$ and $C_2$, added in Fig. 6.10 to isolate successive stages from each other, allowance should also be made for the emitter–base and base–collector capacitances. At low frequencies the reactances of this pair of capacitances can be ignored. For high frequency operation of the transistor they become important and must be taken into account. (It is the charging and discharging of these capacitances which set the upper limit on the frequency at which a device can operate.) At high frequency, therefore, the equivalent circuit of Fig. 6.12 becomes a little more complicated, with $h_{ie}$ and $h_{oe}$ complex impedances rather than simple resistances. This topic will not be pursued further here, but is discussed at length in books on circuit design.

## 6.9 Input and output impedances

Consider a 'black box' amplifier, acting on the voltage from some generator and developing an output across a load $R_L$. Let the generator be of voltage $v_s$ and internal resistance $R_s$, as in Fig. 6.17. It is important in circuit design to know the output impedance across the terminals AB, i.e. the impedance presented by the amplifier to the next stage. Call this $Z_o$. The output

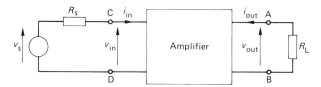

**Fig. 6.17**

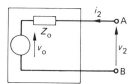

**Fig. 6.18**  Output impedance for circuit of Fig. 6.17

impedance can be calculated quite easily by the use of Thévenin's theorem, which states that any network containing only linear circuit elements and sources can be reduced to an equivalent circuit consisting of one voltage generator in series with one impedance. The idea is expressed in Fig. 6.18, from which it can be seen that if the network chosen is everything to the left of AB in Fig. 6.17, the impedance inside the 'Thévenin box' is the required $Z_o$. The rules for finding $Z_o$ for the circuit of Fig. 6.17 are as follows.
  (i)  Remove everything which follows the terminals AB ($R_L$ in this case).
 (ii)  Replace all external voltage sources by short-circuits and all external current sources by open circuits. Thus $v_s$ is put equal to zero. If the amplifier inside the black box has the equivalent circuit of Fig. 6.16, however, the voltage generator $h_{re}v_{ce}$ and the current generator $h_{fe}i_b$ are not put to zero, since they do not count as 'external' sources; they serve to model the internal action of the transistor.
(iii)  Apply a voltage $v_2$ to the terminals AB and either measure or calculate the current $i_2$. Then $Z_o = v_2/i_2$.
    If the equivalent circuit of the amplifier concerned contains only resistive elements, as in Fig. 6.16, then the output impedance is, of course, purely resistive and $Z_o$ becomes $R_o$.

The input impedance as seen by the source can be calculated in exactly the same way, as indicated in Fig. 6.19. In this case the input impedance is given by $Z_i = v_1/i_1$.

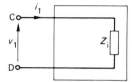

**Fig. 6.19** Input impedance for circuit of Fig. 6.17

## 6.10 Problems

Problems marked * are considered in the computer package (see Preface).

**6.1*** The collector characteristics of a BC 109 transistor are described by the values of the collector current in mA given for various base currents $I_B$ and collector–emitter voltages $V_{ce}$ in the following table:

| $V_{ce}$ | 0.5 | 1 | 1.5 | 2 | 2.5 | 3 | 3.5 | 4 |
|---|---|---|---|---|---|---|---|---|
| $I_B = 100\,\mu A$ | 20 | 24 | 25 | 26 | 27 | 28 | 29 | 30 |
| $200\,\mu A$ | 30 | 37 | 42 | 45 | 49 | 52 | 55 | 57 |
| $300\,\mu A$ | 40 | 48 | 55 | 60 | 65 | 70 | 74 | 78 |
| $500\,\mu A$ | 54 | 65 | 73 | 81 | 88 | 95 | 102 | 108 |

The transistor has its emitter connected to ground and the collector is connected through a load resistor $R_c$ of 30 Ω to a 3-volt supply. Draw the characteristics and plot a load line. Locate an operating point for a base current of $I_B = 200\ \mu A$ and find the output voltage and current swing for a base current swing of $\pm 50\ \mu A$.

Assuming the base current remains constant at $200\ \mu A$, what is the output impedance of the transistor alone? How does $R_c$ affect the output resistance? The maximum power dissipated in the transistor is to be 200 mW. Plot the locus of maximum power on the characteristics. Keeping $I_B = 200\ \mu A$, suggest suitable values for the supply voltage and $R_c$ for the transistor to work at maximum power.

**6.2** A germanium transistor, $h_{FE} = 29$, is connected in the circuit below. If

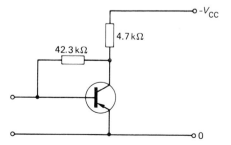

$I_{CBO}$ at 25°C is 10 $\mu$A and doubles for every rise of 9°C, by how much will $V_{CE}$ change if the temperature rises to 52°C? Neglect changes in $V_{BE}$ and $h_{FE}$.

**6.3**  A transistor used in a grounded emitter circuit with a load resistance of 25 k$\Omega$ is fed from a signal generator which has an internal resistance of 600 $\Omega$. Calculate the voltage and current gains of the circuit.

$$h_{ie} = 1\,\text{k}\Omega; h_{oe} = 38.4 \times 10^{-6}\,\text{S}; h_{fe} = 32.3; h_{re} = 8.4 \times 10^{-4}$$

**6.4**  A single-stage common-emitter amplifier is designed using a transistor with the following parameters:

$$h_{fe} = 100, h_{re} = 2 \times 10^{-4}, h_{ie} = 1\,\text{k}\Omega, h_{oe} = 6 \times 10^{-5}\,\text{S}.$$

It is to be used to amplify the signal from a previous stage which has an output resistance of 400 $\Omega$. The supply voltage is 10 V and the load resistance is 10 k$\Omega$. A quiescent base current of about 200 $\mu$A is required.

Calculate the value of the bias resistor needed to attain the stated quiescent point. Calculate also the voltage gain and output impedance of the circuit.

**6.5**  For a common-emitter stage of an amplifier, the collector load is a 3.6 k$\Omega$ resistor and under the bias involved, the *h*-parameters for the transistor are:

$$h_{fe} = 70, h_{ie} = 1.8\,\text{k}\Omega,$$

$$\Delta_e = h_{ie}h_{oe} - h_{re}h_{fe} = 1.1 \times 10^{-3}$$

Calculate the voltage gain. Comment on the significance of the value of $\Delta_e$. What does this imply about the transistor equivalent circuit you are using?

**6.6***  A hi-fi audio pre-amplifier consists of two identical BC 109 transistor common-emitter stages in cascade. Each stage has a 10 k$\Omega$ load resistor and the pre-amplifier is used to amplify a tuner of output impedance 1 k$\Omega$. Calculate the current gain and the output resistance of the pre-amplifier, neglecting the effect of coupling and biasing components.

The *h*-parameters for a BC 109 transistor are

$$h_{ie} = 6.5\,\text{k}\Omega; h_{re} = 2.5 \times 10^{-4}; h_{fe} = 460; h_{oe} = 45 \times 10^{-6}\,\text{S}.$$

**6.7**  Derive the conversion formulae for grounded base hybrid parameters in terms of grounded emitter hybrid parameters. Use realistic approximations which apply to the *h*-parameters of a typical transistor.

**6.8**  An amplifier has a voltage gain of 1000 and a resistive output impedance of 10 k$\Omega$. What value of load impedance will reduce the ratio of output voltage to input voltage to 375? If the amplifier has a resistive input impedance of 1 k$\Omega$ and is connected to a source of internal resistance of 5 k$\Omega$, what is the overall voltage gain?

**6.9**  An amplifier is initially terminated by a load equal to its internal impedance. Derive an expression for the values of load impedance which would cause the power dissipated in the load to fall to half its maximum value. Calculate these values, given that the output impedance has a resistive value of 100 $\Omega$.

# 7 Field Effect Transistors

The term field effect transistor (or FET) describes a class of transistors rather than a single device. These transistors come in a variety of designs and a given type can have a number of different geometries. All of them have a number of features in common, however. They are all three-terminal devices with terminals labelled source, drain and gate, implying that when an FET is used as an amplifier one of the terminals is common to both the input and output sides (the same situation was found for the bipolar transistor in Chapter 6). In addition, the principle of operation of all types is essentially the same. A current is passed through a conducting 'channel' between source and drain. The resistance of the channel can be varied by applying a voltage to the gate terminal. The gate voltage therefore influences the channel current in much the same way as the base current influences the collector current in a bipolar transistor, and amplification can be obtained. The FET can also be used as a switch and is especially important in logic circuits.

In the present chapter we describe the junction field effect transistor (JFET) in some detail and show how it is used in simple amplifying circuits. A brief description is then given of another important type of FET, the insulated gate field effect transistor (IGFET).

## 7.1 The junction field effect transistor

The JFET is illustrated in Fig. 7.1. The particular geometry shown in the diagram has been chosen for ease of explanation; most practical devices have a slightly different form from that indicated. The device shown is symmetrical and consists of a piece of n-type semiconductor into which two p-type regions have been introduced. Source and drain contacts are made at the ends of the device and gate contacts are made to the p-regions. The gates are joined

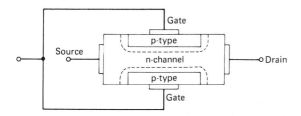

**Fig. 7.1** Junction field effect transistor

together so the transistor effectively has only a single gate contact. Two p–n junctions therefore exist inside the device and, since it is arranged for the p-doping to be much greater than the n-doping, the depletion regions are mostly in the n-type material (see Section 5.2.2). The edges of the depletion regions are indicated by dotted lines on the diagram. The reader will recall that a depletion region is so called because it is depleted of electrons and holes. It follows that such a region has a very high resistance and that the conducting channel between the source and drain consists of the n-type material between the depletion regions.

If a voltage is applied to make the gate terminal negative with respect to the channel, the p–n junctions become reverse-biased and the depletion widths increase (see Section 5.5). The depletion regions therefore encroach further into the channel and the resistance between source and drain increases. In the

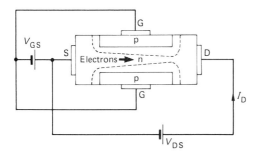

**Fig. 7.2**  JFET with voltages applied to gate and drain

limit the two depletion regions can touch and the conducting channel is removed. The resistance between source and drain then becomes very large and only a minute current can flow along the device. This provides the basis of the operation of the device as a switch; the transistor is 'on' if no voltage is applied to the gate, and 'off' if a large negative voltage is applied.

Now consider the situation shown in Fig. 7.2 in which the gate is made slightly negative with respect to the source, and the drain is made positive. Current will then pass drain–source or, to put it another way, electrons will flow in the opposite direction. The p–n junctions are now reverse-biased for two different reasons; on the one hand the p-sides are made negative by $V_{GS}$ and on the other hand, the n-sides are positive by virtue of $V_{DS}$. Since this second voltage is dropped between S and D, the positive potential of the channel increases between source and drain. This gives the interesting result that the reverse bias on the junctions increases as we go left–right on the diagram. The depletion widths therefore increase, so that the width of the conducting channel is a minimum at the drain end, as shown in Fig. 7.2.

We are now in a position to understand the form of the output characteristic, shown in Fig. 7.3. Suppose for the sake of simplicity that $V_{GS} = 0$ and that $V_{DS}$ is steadily increased from zero. Initially, for low $V_{DS}$, the channel is fairly wide and the behaviour is essentially ohmic, i.e. $I_D \propto V_{DC}$. Increasing $V_{DS}$ causes the depletion regions to move into the channel by substantial amounts, causing the channel resistance to increase. The output current therefore increases sub-linearly with $V_{DS}$. Finally the depletion regions just

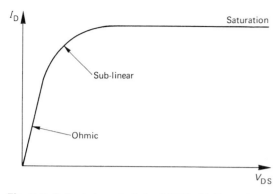

**Fig. 7.3** Output characteristic of JFET with $V_{GS} = 0$

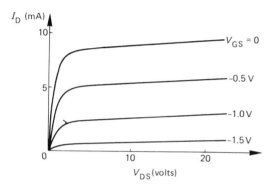

**Fig. 7.4** Set of JFET characteristics, varying $V_{GS}$

touch at the drain end, giving rise to the situation known as 'pinch-off'. The drain current cannot increase further after this point, and the saturation region is reached.

The application of a gate voltage narrows the channel and causes pinch-off to occur at lower values of $V_{DS}$ and $I_D$. A set of output characteristics can therefore be plotted as in Fig. 7.4, each curve corresponding to a different value of $V_{GS}$. The analogy between Fig. 7.4 and the bipolar characteristics shown in Fig. 6.9 is obvious. Just as with the bipolar transistor, the manufacturer's data for a given JFET gives maximum permitted values of $V_{DS}$ and the product $I_D V_{DS}$. The maximum current is limited by the fact that the gate voltage is not permitted to go positive; if this were to occur the p–n junctions would become forward-biased and current would enter the channel from the gate contact. Thus in Fig. 7.4 the maximum current $I_{DMAX}$ is about 10 mA.

## 7.2  Symbols for the JFET

The device described above has an n-type channel. Obviously a similar device could be made with a p-type channel and n-type insertions for the gate. The

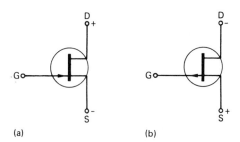

**Fig. 7.5**  JFET symbols, (a) n-channel device, (b) p-channel device

symbols for the two alternatives are shown in Fig. 7.5. Note the arrow in the gate–channel line. It points in the direction p→n, following the convention used for bipolar transistors.

## 7.3  The JFET amplifier

A simple JFET amplifier is shown in Fig. 7.6. The input signal is applied between gate and source and the output is taken between drain and source. The desired working point on the characteristics is achieved by adding the supply $V_{GG}$. This supply must have a resistance $R_1$ in series with it since, it will be remembered, a battery has negligible internal impedance. Without $R_1$, therefore, $V_{GG}$ would present a short-circuit to any applied signal $V_{GS}$. The current flowing through $R_1$ at the working point, $I_G$, corresponds to the reverse current of the gate–channel p–n junction. This is very small, so only a small voltage is developed across $R_1$. The bias voltage applied to the gate is therefore approximately equal to $V_{GG}$.

On the output side we have

$$V_{DD} = I_D R_D + V_{DS} \tag{7.1}$$

and this load line can be plotted on the characteristics of Fig. 7.4. Suppose $V_{DD} = 20$ V, $R_D = 2$ kΩ and $V_{GG} = -1$ V. The working point P is as shown

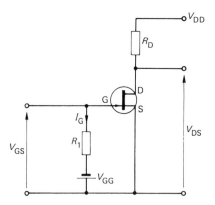

**Fig. 7.6**  Simple JFET amplifier

in Fig. 7.7. It can be seen that if an a.c. input voltage varying between $+0.5$ V and $-0.5$ V is applied to the gate, the operating point moves between the points Q and R, on the diagram. This gives a variation in the output voltage $V_{DS}$ of about $\pm 5$ V, i.e. a voltage amplification of approximately 10.

The considerations concerning distortion previously described for the bipolar transistor apply equally to the JFET. The motion of the operating point along the load line should not take the system out of the region where the characteristics are equally spaced and horizontal.

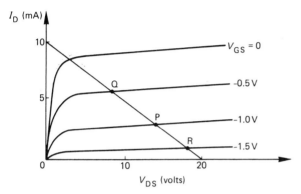

**Fig. 7.7**  Load line plotted on JFET characteristics

## 7.4  Input impedance

At low frequency operation, the input impedance of the JFET is extremely high, of the order of $10^9$ $\Omega$, since it is essentially the resistance of a reverse-biased p–n junction. At high frequencies the capacitance of the junctions must be taken into account (see Section 5.5). In what follows we will assume low-frequency operation so that the input impedance can be assumed effectively infinite.

## 7.5  Small-signal parameters

Since we are assuming infinite input impedance in our model there can be no input current. The equivalent circuit is therefore simpler than the one derived for the bipolar transistor in Chapter 6. The variables are $V_{GS}$, $V_{DS}$ and $I_D$. Expressing changes in $I_D$ in terms of the other two:

$$\delta I_D = \left( \frac{\partial I_D}{\partial V_{GS}} \right)_{V_{DS}} \delta V_{GS} + \left( \frac{\partial I_D}{\partial V_{DS}} \right)_{V_{GS}} \delta V_{DS} \tag{7.2}$$

The second of these partial differentials is the slope of the output characteristic at the working point. It is usually referred to as drain conductance, $g_d$. Its reciprocal is the drain resistance $r_d$. The first partial differential is called the transconductance $g_m$ and is a measure of the change in output current when the gate voltage is varied. Using small letters to indicate small changes, the above equation can be written

$$i_d = g_m v_{gs} + \frac{v_{ds}}{r_d} \qquad (7.3)$$

Equation (7.3) can be described by the equivalent circuit shown in Fig. 7.8.

The small-signal equivalent circuit for the amplifier of Fig. 7.6 is shown in Fig. 7.9. It is a simple matter to find the output impedance of the amplifier, $R_o$,

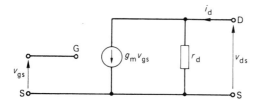

**Fig. 7.8** Small-signal equivalent circuit for JFET

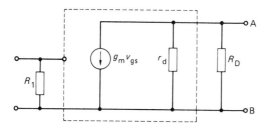

**Fig. 7.9** Equivalent circuit for Fig. 7.6

using the rules given in Section 6.9. The current source $g_m v_{gs}$ becomes an open circuit and the resistance is measured across the output terminals AB. This gives

$$R_0 = \frac{R_D r_d}{R_D + r_d} \qquad (7.4)$$

## 7.6  Biasing the JFET

While the circuit of Fig. 7.6 achieves the object of establishing the desired d.c. operating conditions for the amplifier, it is obviously inconvenient to use two voltage sources for establishing the desired conditions. An alternative to making the gate negative with respect to the source is to make the source positive with respect to the gate. This is done in Fig. 7.10 by the simple expedient of putting in a source resistor $R_s$. The gate is connected to earth through the resistor $R_1$. It has already been pointed out that the current through $R_1$, namely $I_G$, is minute so the voltage dropped across it is small and

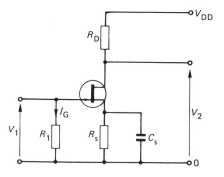

**Fig. 7.10** Use of source resistor in biasing

the gate is approximately at earth potential. The source is therefore positive with respect to the gate by an amount $I_D R_s$. Thus if the drain current is 2 mA and we wish $V_{GS}$ to be $-1.0$ V, a resistance of about 500 $\Omega$ is required for the source resistor.

The resistance $R_s$ is required only to set up the d.c. operating conditions and it is not desirable for any of the a.c. signal to be dropped across it. A capacitance is therefore used in parallel. A value is chosen for $C_s$ to give it a very low reactance at the signal frequency, providing what is effectively a short-circuit for the a.c. signal.

## 7.7  The insulated gate field effect transistor (IGFET)

In this type of transistor the conducting channel is at the surface of the semiconductor chip rather than in the bulk. Because it is a surface device, it lends itself especially well to the 'planar' manufacturing techniques currently used in the semiconductor industry. IGFETs are classified as either 'enhancement' or 'depletion' devices, depending on whether or not a channel exists between source and drain when no voltage is applied to the gate. The devices are sometimes referred to as metal–oxide–semiconductor FETs, or MOSFETs, for reasons which will soon become obvious.

### 7.7.1  Enhancement IGFETs

Fig. 7.11(a) gives the physical form of this type of device. It can be seen that it has a very simple structure. The source and drain regions are two n-type islands in a piece of p-type semiconductor. The gate is a metal contact separated from the semiconductor surface by a thin layer of insulating oxide. A capacitor is therefore formed, with the gate contact and the semiconductor surface as the plates and the oxide as the dielectric.

With no voltage applied to the gate there is no conducting path between source and drain and no current can flow. For this reason the device is sometimes called a 'normally off' transistor. If a positive voltage, $V_{GS}$, is applied to the gate, however, electrons are attracted to the surface and a thin n-type layer is formed there. A conducting channel now exists and if a voltage is applied between source and drain, a drain current flows. The conventional symbol for the n-channel enhancement device is shown in Fig. 7.12. The broken line for the channel indicates a normally-off device. Note that there is a substrate terminal in this case and that the arrow goes p→n in accordance with previous conventions.

Consider the situation, shown in Fig. 7.11(b), when the gate is biased positive and the drain is made positive with respect to the source. The latter voltage, $V_{DS}$, is dropped between source and drain, so the channel becomes progressively more positive. It follows that the voltage between gate and channel decreases as we go left to right on the diagram, so the width of the conducting channel also decreases. This is much the same effect as was found for the JFET. As $V_{DS}$ is increased, the width of the channel at the drain end diminishes until $V_{DS} \simeq V_{GS}$, when it disappears altogether. This is the situation previously referred to as pinch-off and, as before, the drain current $I_D$ saturates at this value of drain voltage. Higher constant values of $V_{GS}$ cause

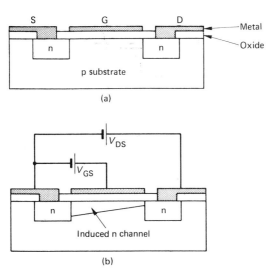

(a)

(b)

**Fig. 7.11** (a) n-channel enhancement IGFET, (b) showing induced channel when device is biased

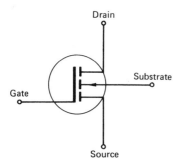

**Fig. 7.12** Circuit symbol for n-channel enhancement IGFET

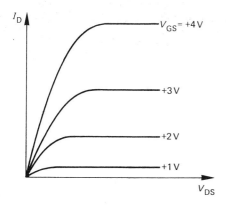

**Fig. 7.13** Output characteristics for n-channel enhancement IGFET

pinch-off to occur at higher values of $I_D$ and $V_{DS}$. The output characteristics for the device are very similar to those for the JFET; a typical set is given in Fig. 7.13.

The equivalent p-channel device can be made by introducing p-type source and drain regions into an n-type substrate. In this case the gate has to be made negative in order to introduce a conducting channel and the drain is biased negative with respect to the source.

### 7.7.2 Depletion IGFETs

If a thin n-type layer is introduced into the surface just beneath the gate, a conducting path exists between source and drain even with no voltage applied to the gate. This type of IGFET, called a depletion or 'normally on' device, is shown in Fig. 7.14 together with its symbol. Note that the line representing the channel is now unbroken.

With $V_{GS} = 0$, current flows in the channel as the drain is made positive with respect to the source. Because $V_{DS}$ is dropped between source and drain, however, the gate is negative with respect to the channel at the drain end. Thus electrons are repelled from the surface at the drain end and the channel narrows, as before. Pinch-off occurs exactly as in the enhancement

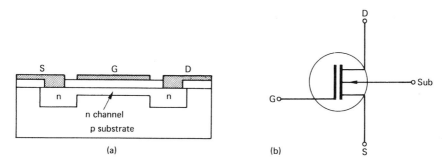

**Fig. 7.14** (a) n-channel depletion IGFET, (b) circuit symbol

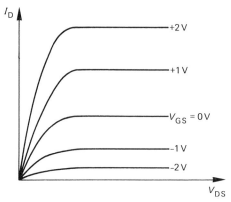

**Fig. 7.15** Output characteristics, n-channel depletion IGFET

device, so a similar output characteristic is obtained, as in Fig. 7.15. With this device, however, the gate can be made either negative or positive. In the former case the width of the conducting channel is decreased, so pinch-off occurs at lower values of $V_{DS}$ and $I_D$. In the latter case the width is increased so pinch-off occurs at higher values of these quantities. A full set of characteristics therefore shows curves on both sides of the $V_{GS} = 0$ characteristic.

As with the enhancement transistor, the complementary device can be made with a p-channel formed in an n-type substrate.

### 7.7.3 Input impedance of IGFETs

The input impedance is that of the metal–oxide–semiconductor capacitor. The oxide used has a very high resistivity, so the resistance at the input is extremely high. Under conditions of high frequency operation, however, the capacitance of the MOS structure must be taken into account.

## 7.8 Problems

Problems marked * are considered in the computer package (see Preface).

**7.1*** A FET is connected into the circuit shown in Fig. Q7.1. The quiescent drain current is 0.5 mA and the output voltage swings about a nominal 12 V with respect to the common line. The gate voltage $V_{GS}$ is 0.9 V. Calculate values for $R_2$ and $R_3$, and also the voltage gain when the output is unloaded. Explain the functions of $R_1$ and $C_2$ and indicate how you would choose values for those components. Assume the following parameters for the FET:

Forward transfer conductance, $g_m = 7 \times 10^{-4}\,\text{S}$,

Output conductance $\qquad r_d = 5 \times 10^{-5}\,\text{S}$.

**7.2** A field effect transistor is used as a voltage amplifier. The transconductance is 4 mS and the load resistor is initially 50 kΩ. When the load resistor is changed to 30 kΩ, the output resistance of the stage is reduced to 80% of the original value. Calculate the voltage gain for both values of the load.

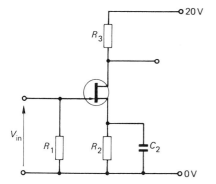

**Fig. Q7.1**

**7.3\*** The characteristics of an n-channel FET can be approximated for $V_{DS} > 2.5$ V by the following table:

| $V_{GS}(V)$ | 0 | $-0.4$ | $-0.8$ | $-1.2$ | $-1.6$ | $-2.0$ | $-2.4$ |
|---|---|---|---|---|---|---|---|
| $I_D(mA)$ | 7.40 | 5.45 | 3.95 | 2.65 | 1.60 | 0.75 | 0.10 |

An amplifier stage is constructed using this transistor, with a drain resistance of 3.3 kΩ and a source resistance of 300 Ω. A d.c. supply of 30 V is used and the gate is connected to the negative supply rail through a resistor of high value. Find the drain current and the voltage dropped across the transistor at the quiescent state of the amplifier (i.e. with no applied a.c. signal).

**7.4** A field effect transistor has a small-signal equivalent circuit with the parameters

Forward transfer conductance $= 4\,mS$,
Output conductance $\qquad = 100\,\mu S.$

The operating point for the circuit is defined by

$V_{DS} = +4$ V

$V_{GS} = -2$ V

$I_D = 2\,mA$

Draw the circuit you would use for a single stage voltage amplifier, specifying the values of as many components as possible, assuming a 30 V supply is available. What voltage gain is obtained when the output is unloaded?

**7.5** A field effect transistor is used as a voltage amplifier and with a load resistor of 40 kΩ a gain of 40 is obtained. If the load resistor is halved, the voltage gain drops to 30. Calculate the output resistance and the mutual conductance of the transistor.

# 8 Integrated Circuits: the Operational Amplifier

So far we have considered amplifying circuits involving individual devices. One of the wonders of modern semiconductor technology is that whole circuits, composed of many transistors, diodes, resistors etc., can be integrated on a single chip. In a great many applications in electronics the basic building block is the integrated circuit rather than the transistor. A variety of different types of integrated circuit is now available, covering a multitude of applications. Only a few such applications can be considered here and discussion will be limited to the class of integrated circuits known as operational amplifiers. These devices are so called because they are able to perform a number of mathematical operations on input signals. They are essentially low-frequency amplifiers of very high gain. The circuit of an operational amplifier is quite complex, containing perhaps twenty or more transistors with associated resistors and capacitors.

## 8.1 The operational amplifier

Before describing this device in detail, it is interesting to consider the characteristics which an 'ideal' voltage amplifier would be required to have. Fig. 8.1 shows an amplifier acting on an input (represented by a voltage source and a series resistance) and developing an output across some load $R_L$. The amplifier itself is represented by Thévenin equivalent circuits on both the input and output sides. Looked at from the input side, the amplifier presents an input resistance $R_i$, while from the output side it is seen as a voltage source $Av_{in}$, where $A$ is the gain of the amplifier, in series with an output resistance $R_o$. The voltage $v_s$ is dropped partly across $R_s$ and partly across $R_i$. Only the latter component is amplified so it is desirable for $R_i$ to be large. For similar

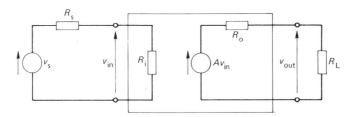

**Fig. 8.1** Equivalent circuit for a 'black box' amplifier

reasons, we wish $R_o$ to be as small as possible, since the output of the amplifier is required across $R_L$ rather than $R_o$. Finally, it is obviously desirable that $A$ should be as large as possible.

The operational amplifier is different in one important respect from the one shown in Fig. 8.1; it has two inputs rather than one and it is the difference between the two which is amplified. In other respects it approximates closely to the 'ideal' amplifier. The 741 type, for instance, has the typical characteristics: $R_i = 2$ MΩ, $R_o = 75$ Ω, $A = 2 \times 10^5$. For many purposes the input impedance can be taken as effectively infinite and the output impedance can be assumed equal to zero. When these approximations are made, the circuit

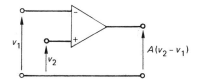

**Fig. 8.2** Circuit symbol for operational amplifier

symbol shown in Fig. 8.2 is appropriate. The two inputs are known as 'inverting' and 'non-inverting' and, taking due regard of the signs associated with them, it is the algebraic sum of the inputs which is amplified. The lack of any internal connection between the two inputs is a consequence of the infinite input impedance. In addition to the terminals shown in the figure, the operational amplifier also has terminals for the power supply (usually in the range 5 V–30 V) and many have terminals for various offset voltages.

Although the gain of the device is very high, it is important to realise that it cannot be used to obtain very high voltages, since it is not possible to produce an output voltage greater than that of the power supply. In fact the amplifier saturates at an output voltage just below this. In practice the operational amplifier provides an interesting example of how high gain can be used for purposes other than amplification.

## 8.2 The inverting amplifier

In this configuration, shown in Fig. 8.3, the signal is applied to the inverting input terminal and the non-inverting terminal goes to earth. The feedback resistor $R_2$ joins the input and output sides and has the effect of reducing the overall gain but introduces stability to the circuit.

Consider first the potential $v_x$ at the point X. According to the rule indicated above, we have

$$v_2 = A(0 - v_x) \tag{8.1}$$

since the non-inverting terminal is earthed, i.e.

$$v_x = -\frac{v_2}{A} \tag{8.2}$$

It has been noted above that $v_2$ can only be, at most, of the order of volts and that $A$ is a very large number. It follows that $v_x$ must be extremely small. The point X is therefore referred to as a 'virtual earth' since, to a good degree of approximation, it is held at zero potential while not actually being connected to earth.

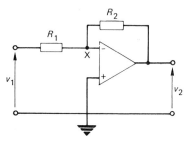

**Fig. 8.3** Inverting amplifier

Because of the infinite resistance between the inputs the current in $R_1$ is the same as that in $R_2$, i.e.

$$i = \frac{v_1 - 0}{R_1} = \frac{0 - v_2}{R_2} \tag{8.3}$$

giving overall gain

$$\frac{v_2}{v_1} = -\frac{R_2}{R_1} \tag{8.4}$$

where the negative sign indicates a phase change of 180° between input and output.

Equation (8.4) gives the remarkable result that the amplification is determined entirely by the value of the input and feedback resistors. The reason for this, of course, is that the virtual earth approximation effectively assumes the gain of the operational amplifier to be infinite. However, $A$ is sufficiently large in practice to make equation (8.4) a good approximation and the equation illustrates the fact that if stable resistors are used, a stable and well-defined amplifier is obtained. Variations in temperature, for instance, might cause changes in $A$, but this will not affect the overall amplification if $R_1$ and $R_2$ remain stable. Similarly, devices which are nominally identical are likely to have slightly different values of $A$, so it is not possible for the designer to assume a precise value. With the circuit of Fig. 8.3 this is unimportant; the only requirement is that $A$ should be very large.

## 8.3 The non-inverting amplifier

In this circuit the signal is applied to the non-inverting terminal, as in Fig. 8.4. The gain can be calculated as follows:

Potential at inverting terminal     $= v_x$

Potential at non-inverting terminal $= v_1$

$$\therefore \quad v_2 = A(v_1 - v_x) \tag{8.5}$$

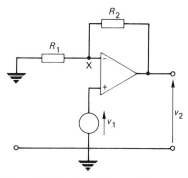

**Fig. 8.4** Non-inverting amplifier

Since $v_2$ is dropped across $R_1$ and $R_2$, which are effectively in series, we can write

$$v_x = \frac{R_1 v_2}{R_1 + R_2} \tag{8.6}$$

From equations (8.5) and (8.6),

$$\frac{v_2}{v_1} = \frac{R_1 + R_2}{\dfrac{R_1 + R_2}{A} + R_1} \tag{8.7}$$

and, for very large $A$,

$$\frac{v_2}{v_1} \simeq 1 + \frac{R_2}{R_1} \tag{8.8}$$

Once again, the over-all amplification is determined by the values of resistance. Note that the output is in phase with the input in this case.

## 8.4  Some further uses of operational amplifiers

### 8.4.1  The summing amplifier

This circuit, shown in Fig. 8.5, may be used to add together a number of inputs. It is essentially an inverting amplifier with a number of input resistors arranged in parallel. The point X is a virtual earth, as before. Since no current passes between the inverting and non-inverting terminals, the current through $R_4$ must be equal to the sum of the currents $i_1$, $i_2$, $i_3$.

$$\frac{v_1 - 0}{R_1} + \frac{v_2 - 0}{R_2} + \frac{v_3 - 0}{R_3} = \frac{0 - v_4}{R_4} \tag{8.9}$$

i.e.

$$v_4 = -R_4 \left( \frac{v_1}{R_1} + \frac{v_2}{R_2} + \frac{v_3}{R_3} \right) \tag{8.10}$$

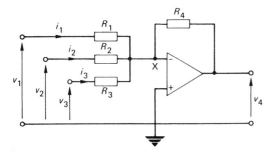

**Fig. 8.5** Summing amplifier

so, apart from the negative sign, the output voltage is a weighted sum of the inputs. Obviously if all four resistors are equal, then

$$v_4 = -(v_1 + v_2 + v_3) \tag{8.11}$$

### 8.4.2 The integrator

The output from this circuit is the integral of the input. The feedback resistor is replaced by a capacitor, as shown in Fig. 8.6. The point X is a virtual earth and the current through $R$ is the same as that through $C$, so that

$$i = \frac{v_1 - 0}{R} \tag{8.12}$$

Voltage across $C$ is $-v_2$, so current is also given by

$$i = -C\frac{dv_2}{dt} \tag{8.13}$$

From equations (8.12) and (8.13)

$$C\frac{dv_2}{dt} = \frac{v_1}{R} \tag{8.14}$$

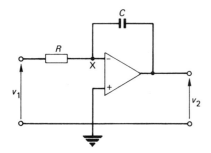

**Fig. 8.6** Integrating circuit

Integrating both sides with respect to $t$ gives

$$v_2 = -\frac{1}{RC} \int v_1 \, dt \qquad (8.15)$$

A common use of this circuit is to provide a linear ramp. This is achieved by applying a constant voltage, $V$, to the input. Equation (8.15) becomes

$$v_2 = -\frac{Vt}{RC} \qquad (8.16)$$

i.e. the output varies linearly with time (until, of course, it almost reaches the supply voltage, and saturates).

### 8.4.3  The differentiator

If the resistance and capacitance are interchanged in Fig. 8.6, a circuit is obtained for which the output is proportional to the differential of the input. It is left as an exercise for the reader to show that

$$v_2 = -RC\frac{dv_1}{dt} \qquad (8.17)$$

### 8.4.4  Analogue circuits

By using the various configurations described in this chapter it is fairly easy to design circuits which carry out more than one of the operations of addition, multiplication, differentiation, integration etc. Thus the performance of a circuit can model the behaviour of the variables in a differential equation, for instance. The variables in the analogue circuit are, of course, voltage and time. Provision must be made in the design to give the required starting voltages at time $t = 0$. This can be done by connecting d.c. voltages to the appropriate points of the circuit to give the required starting conditions. In mathematical terms, this amounts to setting up the boundary conditions. Examples of this type of circuit are given in the problems at the end of the chapter.

## 8.5  Problems

Problems marked * are considered in the computer package (see Preface).

**8.1**  You are provided with an operational amplifier of very large amplification, effectively infinite input impedance and negligible output impedance. Also available are the following components:

| | | | | |
|---|---|---|---|---|
| Resistors: | 1 k$\Omega$, | 10 k$\Omega$, | 100 k$\Omega$, | 1 M$\Omega$; |
| Capacitors: | 0.1 $\mu$F, | 1 $\mu$F, | 10 $\mu$F. | |

Using such of these as are necessary, design
(a) a circuit which provides an amplification of $-100$;
(b) a circuit with an output voltage of $V_o$ given by

$$V_0 = -0.1 \int V_i dt,$$

where $V_i$ is the input voltage.

Show from first principles that each of these circuits will behave in the manner indicated, taking care to distinguish between the two inputs of the amplifier.

**8.2**  An operational amplifier has a voltage gain, $A$, of $2 \times 10^3$ and input resistance $R_i$. It is connected as an inverting amplifier with an input resistor of value 1 kΩ and a feedback resistor of $R_f$. Calculate the overall voltage gain for the following values of $R_i$ and $R_f$, without making the assumption that $A$ is 'effectively infinite'.

(i) $R_i = \infty$,        $R_f = 4$ kΩ

(ii) $R_i = \infty$,        $R_f = 400$ kΩ

(iii) $R_i = 1$ kΩ,        $R_f = 4$ kΩ

(iv) $R_i = 1$ kΩ,        $R_f = 400$ kΩ.

**8.3\***  Newton's law of cooling states that the rate of cooling of a hot body is given by

$$\frac{dT}{dt} = -k(T - T_A)$$

where $T$ is the temperature of the body and $T_A$ is the ambient temperature. Design an analogue system which models the equation.

# Answers to Problems

## Chapter 1

1  $6.6 \times 10^{-34}$ J s, 3.12 V.
2  (a) 1; (b) $5.3 \times 10^{-11}$ m; (c) $1.1 \times 10^{-34}$ kg m$^2$ s$^{-1}$; (d) $2.0 \times 10^{-24}$ kg m s$^{-1}$; (e) $4.1 \times 10^{16}$ rad s$^{-1}$; (f) $2.2 \times 10^{6}$ m s$^{-1}$; (g) $8.2 \times 10^{-8}$ N; (h) $9.0 \times 10^{22}$ m s$^{-2}$; (i) 13.6 eV; (j) $-27.2$ eV; (k) $-13.6$ eV.
3  14.1 eV; 0.5 eV.
4  $3.0 \times 10^{-12}$ m; 91 V.
5  $3.9 \times 10^{-12}$ m.
6  $2.65 \times 10^{-11}$ m.

## Chapter 2

1  1; 2; 4.
2  54.7°; 54.7°; 0.17 nm.
3  Unit cube 0.28 nm; (100) 0.14 nm; (110) 0.10 nm; (111) 0.16 nm; 30°; 44.4°; 25.9°.
4  0.56.
5  26.3°.
6  0.40 nm.

## Chapter 3

1  $8.5 \times 10^{28}$ m$^{-3}$; $7.4 \times 10^{-7}$ m s$^{-1}$.
3  $2.37 \times 10^{-14}$ s (Cu); $3.79 \times 10^{-14}$ s (Ag).

## Chapter 4

1  (a) $-2.2 \times 10^{-2}$ m$^3$ C$^{-1}$; (b) 83.8 V m$^{-1}$ in negative $y$-direction; (c) 5.59 V; (d) 0.34 V.
2  p-type; 1.04 $\mu$g; p-type; 6.38 $(\Omega$m$)^{-1}$.
3  $8.0 \times 10^{20}$ m$^{-3}$; 0.245 eV below conduction band;
   $8.0 \times 10^{22}$ m$^{-3}$; 0.125 eV below conduction band;
   $1.6 \times 10^{21}$ m$^{-3}$; 0.21 eV above valence band;
   $1.6 \times 10^{23}$ m$^{-3}$; 0.092 eV above valence band.

**4**   $Ge: 0.33 \times 10^{20} \, m^{-3}, 2.3 \times 10^{20} \, m^{-3}, 9.8 \times 10^{20} \, m^{-3}$;
   $Si: 5.58 \times 10^{15} \, m^{-3}, 1.33 \times 10^{17} \, m^{-3}, 1.44 \times 10^{18} \, m^{-3}$;
   $Ge: 0.068 \, \Omega m, 0.016 \, \Omega m$;
   $Si: 83.9 \, \Omega m, 7.76 \, \Omega m$.

**5**   (i) $8.7 \times 10^{20} \, m^{-3}$; $54 \, (\Omega m)^{-1}$, (ii) $3.4 \times 10^{20} \, m^{-3}$; $11 \, (\Omega m)^{-1}$;
   (iii) $5.3 \times 10^{20} \, m^{-3}$; $33 \, (\Omega m)^{-1}$.

**6**   $456 \, \Omega$; $157.5 \, \Omega$.

**7**   $6.05 \times 10^{23} \, m^{-3}$ (n); $1.26 \times 10^{8} \, m^{-3}$ (p); $1.21 \times 10^{24} \, m^{-3} \, (N_D)$;
   $1.17 \times 10^{24} \, (N_A)$.

**8**   $1.7 \times 10^{-21} \, J$; $4.2 \, nm$.

# Chapter 5

**1**   $0.58 \, eV$; $1.94 \, V$.

**2**   $0.68 \, eV$.

**3**   $1.5 \times 10^{22} \, m^{-3}$ (n); $4.2 \times 10^{16} \, m^{-3}$ (p); $912 \, (\Omega m)^{-1}$;
   $2.5 \times 10^{16} \, m^{-3}$ (n); $2.5 \times 10^{22} \, m^{-3}$ (p); $720 \, (\Omega m)^{-1}$; $0.335 \, V$.

**5**   $982.33 \, \mu A$.

# Chapter 6

**1**   $1.55$–$1.95 \, V$; $35$–$48 \, mA$; $7 \, mS$; $40 \, mS$; $6 \, V$ (approx.); $44 \, \Omega$.

**2**   $2.3 \, V$.

**3**   $-328$; $16.5$.

**4**   $50 \, k\Omega$; $-490$; $6.9 \, k\Omega$.

**5**   $-140$.

**6**   $-8.0 \times 10^{4}$; $7.3 \, k\Omega$.

**7**   $h_{ib} = \dfrac{h_{ie}}{1 + h_{fe}}$; $h_{fb} = \dfrac{-h_{fe}}{1 + h_{fe}}$; $h_{ob} = \dfrac{h_{oe}}{1 + h_{fe}}$; $h_{rb} = \dfrac{h_{ie} h_{oe}}{1 + h_{fe}} - h_{re}$.

**8**   $6 \, k\Omega$; $62.5$.

**9**   $17 \Omega$; $583 \, \Omega$.

# Chapter 7

**1**   $1.8 \, k\Omega$; $16 \, k\Omega$; $-6.2$.

**2**   $-75$; $-60$.

**3**   $3.3 \, mA$; $18.1 \, V$.

**4**   $12 \, k\Omega$ (drain load); $1 \, k\Omega$ (source bias); $-21.8$.

**5**   $20 \, k\Omega$; $3 \, mS$.

# Chapter 8

**2**   (i) $3.99$; (ii) $333.2$; (iii) $3.98$; (iv) $285.6$.

# Index